500

D1094623

Modern Science and the
Genesis Record

Modern Science and the Genesis Record

BY

HARRY RIMMER, D.D., Sc.D.

WM. B. EERDMANS PUBLISHING COMPANY
GRAND RAPIDS, MICHIGAN

MODERN SCIENCE AND THE GENESIS RECORD
BY HARRY RIMMER, D.D., Sc.D.

Copyright 1937 *by*

RESEARCH SCIENCE BUREAU, INCORPORATED

All rights in this book are reserved. No part of the book may be reproduced in any manner whatsoever without written permission. For information address the publishers.

Eleventh printing, August 1962

PHOTOLITHOPRINTED BY CUSHING - MALLOY, INC.
ANN ARBOR, MICHIGAN, UNITED STATES OF AMERICA

Foreword

THIS Second Volume of the John Laurence Frost Memorial Library continues the series on Apologetics which the author hopes to complete in four more volumes devoted to this work. Like the First Volume, "The Harmony of Science and Scripture," most of this material in Volume Two has not only been used in lecture form before student bodies, scientific and teaching assemblies, as well as the general public, but has also appeared in pamphlet form and in stated editorials in various publications.

These compilations of fact and vindications of Scripture have been blessed of God to the establishment of the faith of thousands. This material is now gathered into the present volume in order that it may be permanently available to all who desire reasons for the hope that is in their hearts.

The reader is, of course, familiar with the New Testament episode of the personal-worker who approached another one saying, "Come and see! We have found Him of whom Moses and the prophets did speak." After His resurrection from the dead, the Lord Jesus opened the eyes of His apostles to all that was written concerning Himself by Moses and the prophets. Therefore, in all that Moses wrote, there must be a foreshadowing of the person and work of Jesus Christ. We do not attempt to study the book of Genesis purely for its scientific value. We approach the study from that angle only that we may have additional illumination on the person and work of our Saviour. Therefore, each of the studies in these work-days of God is concluded with a picture of Him of whom Moses did speak.

Trusting that the blessing of God may dwell richly upon all who read these pages, this volume is launched to continue the testimony of the John Laurence Frost Memorial Library.

Harry Rimmer.

Contents

CONTENTS

The Prologue to Genesis

Genesis Chapter One

1. <u>In</u> the beginning God created the heaven and the earth.

2. And the earth was without form, and void; and darkness *was* upon the face of the deep. And the Spirit of God moved upon the face of the waters.

CHAPTER ONE

The Prologue to Genesis

THE most bitter contest that has ever been waged has been the current discussion over the credibility of the first chapter of the book of Genesis. For more than fifty years the most brilliant minds that infidelity and modernism (the Siamese twins of Satan's spawning) could marshal to the attack, have been concentrated on this one chapter. Moses has been defamed by these adversaries and contradicted from every conceivable angle because of his statements on the subject of special creation. The most recent attack has been launched against this first chapter of Genesis from the redoubts of modern science, and infidelity in this new disguise has contended for a generation that the facts of science constitute a refutation of this entire chapter. This is a serious indictment indeed, and the modern student is entitled to know the facts. Is it a literal truth that science is at variance with Moses? Indeed it is not; rather the contrary is true: there is such a magnificent and complete agreement between the established facts of physical science and the first chapter of Genesis that no human explanation of this strange phenomenon is possible. How is it to be explained on any natural basis? Here is a chapter of a book written in the fifteenth century before Christ, in a day of ignorance and superstition. Yet when we examine that book in the light of modern scientific discoveries, it contains the most recent facts of physics, botany, astronomy and kindred sciences; and has maintained this marvelous harmony with scientific truth for ages before these sciences were born.

The entire Bible is able to hold its own in any kind of a controversy with human wisdom in any form, and of no part

of the Bible is this more true than of the first chapter of Genesis. In the course of this volume we shall consider, one by
one, the Days of Creation in the chapter in question, and shall
array the facts of science upon the witness stand and allow
each to testify. But in the very beginning we must clear the
atmosphere by a consideration of the most perplexing question that is ever raised about this chapter; namely, the time
element implied in each of these creative days. There is one
question that we are certain to meet in every such discussion as
this, and that question is, *Are the Days of Genesis literal days
of twenty-four hours each, or are they periods of time?*

To that question we can only reply, "we do not know":
and then set forth the evidence that shows also why we *cannot
know*.

This word *"day"* is one of the mysteries of Scripture. There
is no scholar living so erudite that he can be dogmatic here. It
is possible that this word "day" will continue to baffle the student unless some new source of light shall be discovered. The
word day in the English Bible is of course not the word Moses
used in his original writing, as Moses wrote in Hebrew, and
knew nothing of the English tongue. The word Moses used
in the Hebrew inscriptions is *"yom,"* and we desire to emphasize again that it is impossible to dogmatize in stating its
meaning. To show how complicated the case here is, we will
state that this word "yom" appears in the Hebrew text of the
Old Testament one thousand four hundred and eighty different times! *and is translated into the English in our Bible by
no less than fifty-four different words.* If, then, the Hebrew
word "yom" can be subject to fifty-four different meanings,
how can we be so dogmatic as to demand a certain unswerving
restriction to only one of those meanings?

To get the matter even more clearly in our minds, let us
look at a few of those possible meanings. The word "yom" is
translated in the Authorized English edition of the Bible:

1181 times as "day" (this covering several meanings) .
  67 times as "time."
  30 times as "today."
  18 times as "forever."
  10 times as "continually."
   6 times as "age."
   4 times as "life."
   2 times as "perpetually."

It is thus absolutely impossible to take any one meaning of the many that are permissible and say, " 'Yom' must be translated thus, and thus only, in every possible case." The rule of translation and interpretation, of course, is that in any case of doubt the meaning must be determined by the translation that is usually given, or perhaps we might say that the law of average governs here. Thus in the case of "yom," since in the overwhelming majority of cases this word is translated by the English equivalent of "day," this translation must be accepted in every case that is not otherwise demanded by the context. But to the word "day," even in the English language, there are many meanings. It may be a solar day, it may be a figure of speech covering considerable time, or it may be a collective word covering a definite number of years. Let us examine some of the Scripture meanings and usages of this word "day," and see what we can determine concerning the time element in the first chapter of Genesis.

1.

The word "yom," or "day," in Scripture, frequently means a solar day as we understand it. Out in space, some ninety millions of miles from this planet, there shines the mighty and majestic orb that we call the sun. It is the source of light, heat, and to a very considerable extent, life. It is surrounded by various satellites, called planets, one of which we inhabit. This planet we call Earth, after the statement in the first of Genesis that this was to be its name. It is not a stationary body, but has various motions inherent in its very creation. One of those motions is called diurnal revolution, which is the rotation of the planet upon its axis from west to east. This speed of rotation is such that it takes approximately twenty-four hours for the planet to make one complete revolution. (The exact time for this revolution is given by astronomers as twenty-three hours, fifty-six minutes, four seconds, and nine-hundredths of a second.) This revolution being performed in the face of the sun, and the Earth being globular in shape, it follows that any given place on the face of this planet will thus experience approximately twelve hours of light from the sun, and twelve hours of darkness, the darkness being occasioned by the fact that the earth's surface on which this given point is situated is away from the sun. This period of light is called "day," and the period of darkness is called "night." For the purposes of the calendar, however, the two periods, light and darkness, are united into one and called a day, or a solar day, to be more exact. This period, then, of twenty-four hours is frequently meant by the Scripture in its use of the word "day," or "yom."

Let us note a few references which will establish this beyond doubt. In Genesis, chapter seven and verse eleven, we read:

"In the six hundredth year of Noah's life, in the second month, on *the seventeenth day of the month, on the same day* were all the fountains of the great deep broken up, and the windows of heaven opened. And the rain was upon the earth forty days and forty nights." Here are two definite meanings of this word "yom," one being a solar day, unquestionably, and the other being daylight, as distinguished from darkness. Again we see in the eighth chapter, verse four:

"And the ark rested in the seventh month, on the *seventeenth day of the month,* upon the mountains of Ararat."

Thus, when the day of the month is referred to, there can be no question as to the meaning of the word in this instance.

It means literally a solar day. It is not necessary to multiply such instances; there are hundreds of verses in the Old Testament, where the word day means a solar day as we know it in our own generation.

2.

Again, the word sometimes means a period of time, of greater or lesser extent, generally of indefinite duration. Such a time period is found in Isaiah the second chapter, where the prophet says:

"For there shall be a day of Jehovah of Hosts upon all that is proud and haughty . . ."

". . . And Jehovah alone shall be exalted in that day . . ."

"In that day men shall cast away their idols . . ."

All through the prophecy of Isaiah this meaning is given in many instances to the word "day," and without presenting too many instances, see the fourth chapter, where the prophet again says:

"And seven women shall take hold of one man in that day, saying, 'We will eat our own bread and wear our own apparel, only let us be called by thy name.' . . ."

"In that day shall the branch of Jehovah be beautiful and glorious . . ."

So then, the word "day," or "yom," is sometimes used in a figurative sense, a time period being intended. There are many such passages where this is so.

3.

In other instances the word "day" means time itself. Thus we read in Genesis, fourth chapter and verse three:

"And in process of time it came to pass . . ."

and we find that in the Hebrew text this word is our study-word, "yom," or day. In chapter twenty-six and verse eight we read again:

"And it came to pass, when he had been there a long time . . ."

and once more this word "yom" appears, but this time instead of being translated day it is translated "a long time." So also we read in Numbers, chapter twenty, verse fifteen:

"And we have dwelt in Egypt a long time . . ." the word "yom" here translated "a long time" covering a span of four hundred and twenty years. Yet this is the same word that appears in the first of Genesis as the creative period, and is called, there, "day."

4.

Another meaning of the word "yom," or "day," must be noted before we pass on to our conclusion as to its meaning. Sometimes the word is used to denote a comprehensive, or inclusive, period. Thus we see that in the first chapter of Genesis the story of creation is given in seven "yoms," or days, or time periods. But in the second chapter of this same book another meaning of "day" appears when the text starts:

"These are the generations of the heaven and of the earth when they were created, in *the day* that Jehovah made heaven and earth."

Here we have the day (yom) embracing in its meaning all the days (yoms) of the first chapter, yet without doing violence to the meaning of the word. We note again in the book of Deuteronomy, chapter ten and verse ten:

"And I stayed in the mount, as at the first time (yom) forty days (yoms) and forty nights, and Jehovah hearkened unto me that time (yom) also."

Here we see the word "yom" used for a solar day, and for forty solar days, and for an occasion, all in the same verse. So there is a wide variety of meanings possible in the use of the word; and it thus becomes impossible to dogmatize as to the meaning of the Creative Days in the Genesis account of creation. If the student desires to accept the era theory, and say that these days were vast periods of time, there is room enough in the Hebrew meaning to allow of this interpretation.

BUT—while we thus conclude that the days of Genesis do not arbitrarily demand a solar day meaning, we must not lose sight of the fact that these days of creation may very well have been solar days.

There are many arguments, and sound ones, which incline some to think that this is indeed the meaning of the text. Let us carefully set forth several reasons why we personally accept the theory that these days of creation were indeed solar days as we know them today.

First: we note that each of these days in Genesis is divided into periods of darkness and light, exactly as a solar day is. These periods, conforming to the custom of the Hebrew people, start and end in the same way: "There was evening; there was morning; one day." This is in exact conformity with the method of recording time used in the day of Moses and in the time of Christ, and in every age since man has been on the face of the earth. A period of light, a period of darkness; each being approximately equal to the other in length of time, and the two periods are called collectively a "day." It may be contended that the first three days could not have been solar days because the rays of the sun did not shine on the earth until the fourth day; but it must be remembered that even today there are many winter days when we never see the sun. *But there is evening and morning just the same,* and we so divide the day even in the absence of the direct light of the sun.

Second: we note that on the third day of Genesis the vast world of botany was born. All the grass, the herbs, the trees and the plants appear later to multiply into their ordained profusion. This third day also is divided as are the other five; light and darkness making one day. For the purpose of our inquiry, let us adopt the theory that this day was a period of geological time; we will concede that this period was some five hundred thousand years, which seems to be the favorite geological guess. At once an insurmountable obstacle to the truth of the narrative arises; we are faced with the thought that the plants must have had two hundred and fifty thousand years of light, and then two hundred and fifty thousand years of darkness. It is an utter impossibility to conceive that the world of botany could have lived half a geological age without the rays of the sun. But if on the other hand these days were solar days, and botany was born on the third of them, the presence of the sun only twenty-four hours later would make the account perfectly consistent with both science and reason.

Third: each different order of living things, although made in one day, did not appear in its present profusion. Of the living creatures a pair of each species was made, a male and a female, and they were charged with the task of multiplying and filling the earth with their own kind. This would be accomplished in a short time under such ideal Edenic conditions. Even at the present rate of reproduction the entire progeny of one pair of field mice, if unmolested, would number over a million in a year. A female mackerel would lay five hundred thousand eggs in one mass of roe, and other creatures even larger numbers. Also we must remember that the various *species only* were created in the beginning, and the infinite numbers of varieties that have since arisen, by mutation, must not be ascribed to the day of the origin of the pure parent of each kind. Thus there is no apparent reason for saying that a solar day would not be sufficient time for the creation or appearance of life as Moses sets it forth, and especially is this so when we remember that we are dealing in this record with the limitless power of an omnipotent God. Of Him it may well be said, "He speaketh, and the thing commanded is accomplished."

Fourth: the Hebrew text implies an instantaneity of accomplishment in each case that would preclude the need of an age factor in explanation of each day. As an instance, if we may anticipate our coming study of that day, on the first day the text states, "Then said God, 'Exist, light!' and light existed." This implies, and in fact states, an instant response to the command in the appearance of light. Why wrest this verse out of all its original meaning and demand five hundred thousand years or more, for the fulfillment of that one Divine command? Would not twenty-four hours be sufficient time for God to accomplish this one thing? Indeed, twenty-four seconds would be many times the amount of time needed as far as omnipotence is concerned. For some reason it pleased the Creator to divide His work-time into "days" and it seems that He consistently followed this plan and division. But in the structure of the Hebrew text, these days are not so stated as to imply eras or aeons; although we must remember that the original word with which we deal may be translated as such.

Fifth: in justification of the idea of a solar day, it must be conceded that Moses intended to convey the idea of a day of twenty-four hours. The science of geology was not born until many thousands of years after Moses wrote, and he was not seeking to state in modern terms the truth he imparted. That the truth always agrees with modern knowledge in spite of its ancient origin is an evidence of the supernatural inspiration of these Mosaic writings, but it is clear that Moses in his explanation meant to convey the idea of a solar day. It may be argued with considerable truth that Moses did not understand the things he wrote, as, like all the other prophets, he must have wondered at many of the revelations that were entrusted to him. But this applies to prophecy, or coming events, and Moses here in the first chapter of Genesis was writing of a past and accomplished fact, so the argument would hardly seem to apply. Intelligent above the average of his own day, or even of ours, Moses sought to convey the thought that God shaped the present creation in six days which were of solar duration, in Moses' own understanding.

Sixth: in the Hebrew manuscripts, when a definite number precedes or accompanies the word "yom," a solar day is intended. Thus we have the seventeenth yom of the month, the seventh yom of the week, the third yom of the journey, the second yom of the feast, and other cases too numerous to mention. Applying this fact to the days of Genesis, we note that there is such a definite number with each of these creative yoms, or days. Evening and morning, one day; two days; and so on to the seventh day, wherein God rested. If we follow strictly the rule of the Hebrew language we must consistently translate these creative days as solar days, as they are each and all preceded by the number, until all seven form a time-period corresponding to our present week, which is certainly to be recognized as seven days of twenty-four hours each. These days as we have them, dividing our year into fifty-two weeks, are so in accord with the creation that now sustains us, and the year thus divided is so nearly accurate with the solar system, that we need only a slight adjustment of our time element once every four years. So the seven day week seems to be sustaining evidence of this Hebrew method of reckoning time, and the adjective that denominates a "yom" as a definite solar day should be strong evidence thereof.

Seventh: in the twentieth chapter of Exodus we have the account of the establishing of the seventh, or Sabbath, day as a day of rest. For many years this had been as any other day in the week, but when God desired a certain covenant sign that would be universally recognized as marking His people as peculiar to Himself, He said·

"Remember the sabbath day, to keep it holy. Six days shalt thou labour, and do all thy work, but the seventh day is a sabbath unto Jehovah thy God; in it thou shalt not do any work, thou, nor thy son, nor thy daughter, thy manservant, nor thy maidservant, nor thy cattle, nor thy stranger that is within thy gates; for *in six days Jehovah made heaven and earth, the sea, and all that in them is, and rested the seventh day; wherefore Jehovah blessed the sabbath day, and hallowed it.*"

This language is clear, and seems strong evidence that these days of creation were literal twenty-four hour days. This sabbath day, the seventh of the week, is set as a type of the one on which God rested, or ceased from His creative work. If we make the creative days geological periods of time, then we must make the rest day, or the seventh of that first "week," an era, if we are to be consistent. In that case God is still resting, as we are still in the same geological period that witnessed the creation of Adam. If God is still in His seventh day, and resting, then it is difficult to explain the statement that Jesus made:

"My meat is to do the will of Him that sent Me, and to finish His work!"

Since this Jesus is the same Person as the Jehovah of creation, and if the seventh day of Genesis is a geological age or era, how does it happen that in the middle, or perhaps the very dawn of that period, the seventh, He suddenly breaks His rest and comes to earth to finish His work? How much more consistent with the entire Scripture is the simple explanation that these days were literal days, and that God rested on the seventh one. This seventh day, the sabbath or rest day, was kept sacred by the Jews to whom it was given as a covenant sign from the time God spoke, to the time of the coming of Christ. It was kept by the early Christian Church, until by the express command of the Holy Spirit, as uttered by the apostle Paul, the day was no longer binding on the children of God. The children of Israel still observe the day, not discerning in the New Testament God's will and revelation for this age in which we live. But it is a solar day that is ever implied in the Bible, under the simple term, "the seventh day."

The eighth argument in favor of the solar day position is the most conclusive of all. The appearance of man is not until the last day of this week, which, if the theory of aeons is accepted, would be the sixth geological age of creation. This sixth day, or age, is crowned by the appearance of man, and God's work is done. So man was created in the sixth geological age.

Then this new man occupied the garden for the seventh age, while God rested! Unless we desire to contend that this seventh day was a solar day and all the others were ages, we must accept the fact that man lived as an individual through at least parts of three geological ages, and through all of at least one such age! Expelled from the garden after the rest of the seventh day, it was at the very earliest estimate the eighth day. Allowing the typical geological guess for the duration of an "age," Adam lived part of the sixth age, all of the seventh age, and was alive to leave Eden in the eighth age. Then Adam was at least seven hundred and fifty thousand years old when he was expelled from Eden! Such reasoning is folly: how much better just to accept the simple meaning of the evident intention of the text, and call these solar days.

Finally, there is no reason to *demand* an extensive time-period in the days of creation in Genesis, except the desire to be in conformity with the contentions and demands of the evolutionary school of geology. That system of philosophy requires unlimited ages for the unfolding and the gradual development of the creation as it now is and long has been, and calls for multiplied millions of years for each small change in the vast chain of evolving creatures. Hence, it seems necessary to many to acknowledge that the days of Genesis are geological ages, but the fact is, it is necessary only if the evolutionists are right! And in view of the fact that they are uniformly *wrong* on all their other points, why must we make the Bible conform to their age-factor at the cost of reason, and at the price of straining the text?

For these reasons, then, and because we have learned something of the unlimited power and ability of our God, whose only limitation is His own sovereign will and desire, we are inclined to accept the days of Genesis as solar days, as we believe Moses intended them to be understood. At the same time we dare not be dogmatic; and wish to emphasize once more the philological fact, that the word used is susceptible of other meanings, as we showed at the beginning of this chapter.

While we are on this discussion, let us note that whether the "days" are solar or epochal, there are points where geology and Genesis are in remarkable agreement. It is a matter of scientific agreement that the present orders or species of life appear on the earth at the close of the Pleistocene period. That is the last geological age preceding man's appearance, and here Genesis and geology are in absolute accord, as Moses says that God created the animals just prior to the creation of man. Let us note also that the first four days of Genesis are not records of *creation* as that word is commonly understood, but a statement of the release of forces previously in existence, or the assembling of matter or material previously prepared. We shall see this plainly in the discussion of the acts of the various days, in the course of this and the following chapters.

The creation story in Genesis makes use of two contrasting words that are often confused in the English translation of the Bible, and are translated into English by the equivalents, "make" and "create." The first of these words we notice in our study is the Hebrew word "asah," which means to make, to allow, or to assemble. This is the word that would be used to describe the production of a piece of furniture by a carpenter, or the assembling of a motor by a skilled mechanic. In the case of the carpenter it would not be proper to say he had "created" a table: he merely manufactured the article out of materials which were already in existence. It would be equally wrong to say that the mechanic had created a motor which he had assembled: "creation" implies the original production of matter where there was none before; and that is a procedure beyond the power of puny man! The word "asah" also means to release from restraint, and in the first few verses of the Genesis account of the First Week of our present time-period, this word to "make" or to "allow" is the characteristic term used, thus implying that the works of the first days of Genesis

are not an original creation, but the releasing from restraint
of certain materials that were under bondage.

This word "asah" is used in the first chapter of Genesis for
the account of the production of everything except the original
creation in the first verse, and the creation of sentient life.

Here we meet another Hebrew word, of totally different significance; the word "bara." This word appears in the Hebrew
text fifty-five times, and always means the instant, miraculous
creation of something which had no previous existence in any
form whatever. The word "bara" is translated into the English
Bible thirty-three times as "create," nine times as "created,"
and three times as "Creator." The other references do not apply to this study, as in the remaining ten references there is a
qualifying phrase used with the word "bara" which establishes
its meaning in those particular cases. The common use of the
word in Hebrew, however, is the equivalent of the absolute
meaning of the English word "create."

The first appearance of this word "bara" in the Hebrew
text is in the first verse of the first chapter of Genesis:

"In the beginning God created (bara) the heaven and
the earth."

This is a simple statement of the primal creation, and ascribes
to God the original creation, the primary construction of every
physical thing. The clear meaning is that things began when
God made them out of nothing that was or ever had been!
This verse and this work of origination are not to be confused
with the work of the *First Week,* as we shall be careful to point
out as we advance with this study. We are dealing in the first
chapter of Genesis with two stupendous events, and we must
not confuse them, or chaos will result in our thinking.

The word "bara" does not appear in the text after the first
verse, until the twenty-first verse is reached, where we read:

"And God created (bara) the great sea monsters, and
every living creature that moveth, wherewith the waters

swarmed after their kind, and every winged bird after its
kind; and God saw that it was good."

Here we see the sovereign power of God associated with the
production of something which had never previously been in
existence; that is, animal life. This word "bara" appears also
in connection with the creation of man, and the word is consistently used in every subsequent Scriptural reference to that
tremendous event! Why do these two words stand in such apparent contrast in the first chapter of Genesis, and what is the
significance of the use of two such contrasting words?

It is apparent, to the careful student, that the first verse of
Genesis refers to a work of origination which antedates the
Creative Week with which Moses deals. Indeed, the Scripture
carefully states that originally the creation was far different
from that described in the first chapter of Genesis, in that suggestive second verse:

"And the earth was waste and void, and darkness was
upon the face of the deep, and the Spirit of God brooded
upon the face of the waters."

Contrast this statement of a condition with the following from
Isaiah, chapter forty-five and verse eighteen:

"For thus saith Jehovah that created the heavens, the
God that formed the earth and made it, that established
it and created it *Not a Waste*,—that formed it to be inhabited."

Is this a contradiction between Isaiah and Moses, or are there
two separate subjects under consideration? That matter can
best be settled by a careful study of the first verse quoted above,
namely, the second verse of Genesis. The first verse contents
itself with a simple statement of a consummated act: "In the
beginning God created the heaven and the earth." Not a word
about the method, manner, means or procedure of creation,
and nothing of its result. The second verse carries a tremendous suggestion of collapse in its touching picture of the Spirit

of God brooding over the aqueous face of the creation! Let us see what a careful word-study of this second verse will yield.

In the Authorized Version the text begins: *"And* the earth was . . ."* This word in the Hebrew text is also translated "but," or "moreover." Thus in the Septuagint version of the Scripture the text begins: *"But* the earth had become . . ."* and this is the sense of the Vulgate as well. The second word to be noted is the one translated in the English Bible "was." The Hebrew language lacks a word for "became," so the word "was" is always used to carry out the sense of "became." This phrase then literally reads, *"But the earth had become* . . ." "Tohu v'bohu!"*

This phrase, "tohu v'bohu," is translated in the American Revision "waste and void." In the Authorized Version it reads, "without form and void," but the sense of this phrase is even stronger than that. The Chaldee version states, "But the earth had become desert and empty." The Septuagint says, "But the earth had become unfurnished and empty," the Vulgate says "dreary and empty," and the Aramaic makes the strongest and clearest statement of all: "And the earth had become ruined and uninhabited!" Hebrew scholars, such as Dr. Robert Dick Wilson, have said that this is the clearest statement of all, as the term "tohu v'bohu" literally means "desolation succeeding previous life."

The second verse of Genesis, then, literally should read, "But the earth had become desolate, ruined and unfurnished, covered with water and shrouded with darkness. And the Spirit of God brooded over the face of the waters." Let us clearly keep in mind that all this is *prior* to the first week of creation. Isaiah says that God created the earth *not* a waste and Moses states that the earth nevertheless *had become* a waste.

Why? Is there any hint in the Scriptures that will give us light here? We believe there is, but a hint only. In the first place, Ezekiel describes that primal creation, which is a different creation, and has a different aspect from the first landscape that emerges from the First Week of Genesis. We find this description in the twenty-eighth chapter of Ezekiel, where the prophet addresses God's message to a person he calls "the King of Tyre." That this was not the human personality who then occupied the throne is clearly seen from the prophet's description of him. He is called "the anointed cherub of the covering:" which no human ever could be called. It is stated he was "in Eden, the garden of God," and Adam was the only *man* of whom that could be said. He was set "upon the holy mountain of God" and that could be true only of an angelic being. His spiritual nature is further shown by the description "perfect from the day thou wast created, until evil was found in thee." Isaiah, the prophet, clearly tells us who this being was when he addresses him and says, "How art thou fallen from heaven, O Lucifer, son of the morning!"

This being, then, whom Isaiah calls Lucifer, and who Ezekiel says was the power controlling the king of Tyre, was in the primal Eden. Ezekiel describes that Eden, and it is not the Eden Adam inhabited. That second Eden was a botanical kingdom, but the landscape of the first Eden was all mineral! Read Ezekiel's words:

"Thou wast in Eden, the garden of God. Every precious stone was thy covering, the ruby, the topaz, the diamond, the beryl, the onyx, the jasper, the sapphire, the emerald, the carbuncle, and gold."

What a gorgeous place that must have been! This marvelous description is unequalled by any other in Scripture, except the prophetic description of the new "Eden" to come, where the Redeemed of God are established in an environment where all these mineral wonders surround them again, and where the brilliant beauty is softened and toned down by the most exquisite things that the realm of botany contains.

Putting together, then, the suggestive references of Isaiah, Ezekiel, and Jeremiah, we arrive at the reason for the sudden choas that swept the earth which God created "not empty and unfurnished!" Why did it so become? The answer is in Ezekiel's stern charge, "Thou wast perfect from the day thou wast created, *until iniquity was found in thee!*" Here is the answer: sin! Lucifer, a being of wonderful beauty and wisdom, rebelled against God, his Creator, and sought to establish himself as the Creator's equal, at least. For this sin of rebellion he was hurled from his high place, the angels whom Jude mentions, who followed him, were "bound in the chains of judgment" and the earth which was the scene of this rebellion "*became* waste and chaotic," with the Eternal Spirit of God brooding over the scene of Lucifer's failure. This is not advanced as an original thought. Many eminent Bible teachers hold this view and many more are coming to accept it as the explanation of the chaotic upheaval which the earth experienced at one time.

The original creation of the heaven and the earth, then, is covered in the first verse of Genesis. Only God knows how many ages rolled by before the ruin wrought by Lucifer fell upon the earth, but it may have been an incalculable span of time. Nor can any student say how long the period of chaos lasted; there is not even a hint given. But let us clearly recognize in these studies, that Moses, in the record of the First Week of Creation, is telling the story of God's reconstruction; rather than the story of an original creation. Therefore Moses uses the word "asah," to manufacture, to form, to release from restraint, or to make, rather than the word "bara," to create, until he reaches that part of his narrative where *life appears,* and he then turns to the latter word. It is natural that if life had previously existed it would have perished in this great upheaval when the earth was made "waste and empty," and the new orders God produced must come from pure creative action. It has been suggested that the manifold fossils the rocks contain may be a relic of that pre-Adamic age; but of this no man can know definitely.

There is one place, however, where Moses receives the absolute support of modern science; and that is when he says that this present order of life, the earth as we know it now, was preceded by a span of wild chaos, when water prevailed. Moses and science are in perfect agreement here: following a chaotic condition that ruled the entire earth, the present forms of life suddenly, dramatically, and almost as if by magic, appear.

None of our present species of living creatures can be traced back to the Pleistocene period, which is the age just preceding the appearance of man. Moses and geology are in accord on that conclusion.

This vast period which Moses covers in the second verse of Genesis, geology calls the great Ice Age. There is absolute proof in this science that the entire earth once suffered an overwhelming cataclysm, when ice and water covered the entire face of the globe. It may be that this was the period during which "the Spirit of God brooded over the face of the waters." If so, how could Moses have known of this great chaotic period so long before the science of geology discovered the fact, except by Divine inspiration?

Before we seek an answer to that query, let us first establish the fact that eminent men of science *do* agree with Moses that there was the age of chaos. Note again; Moses says, "Prior to the age of Adam, the earth was covered with water." Geology says: "Prior to the appearance of Man, the earth was shrouded with water."

Citations From Scientists:

Dana: "The accumulation of ice over North America must at least have been four to five thousand feet thick, with hundreds of feet of snow above this."

Agassiz: "During the greatest expanse of the ice fields, there were but few mountain peaks rising above them; where the mountains were below six thousand feet, the ice seems to have passed entirely over them!"

Dawson: "The drift of glacial deposits in eastern America necessitates the conclusion that, in the period of extreme refrigeration, the greater part of the land was under water, and such hills and mountains as protruded were little 'Greenlands,' covered with ice, and sending down glaciers into the sea. As the glacial period advanced, this latter condition prevailed until the waters stood more than a thousand feet deep over the plains of Europe."

Mantell: "The phenomenon of glacial drift must have been effected when the present dry land was beneath the sea, and the subaqueous currents and icebergs were in active motion."

Murchison: "During the glacial period, the low countries of north Europe were, it is well known, covered by an Arctic sea. In short, . . . Berne must have been covered by waters that bathed the foot of the Alps."

De La Beche: "There appears good evidence that those parts of France adjoining the English Channel, were submerged to a depth of more than a thousand feet."

Jamieson: "I think there is no escaping the conclusion that the whole country was submerged. Observations show that the submergence was not local, but general over the length and breadth of the British Isles."

Page: "In this epoch the mammalia of the Tertiary disappeared, and the land was submerged to the depth of several thousand feet."

Now we must admit, that so far as Moses was concerned, he was absolutely unlearned in modern science. Geology was not dreamed of until several thousands of years after Moses had died: how then is this ancient Book in such marvelous accord with the modern school of geology? It is impossible that Moses could have achieved this knowledge by natural means. Then the only possible explanation is that he, like the other men whose writings are preserved in the pages of the sacred Scripture, "spake as he was moved by the Spirit of God!"

Modern Science
and the First Day of Creation

Genesis Chapter One

3. And God said, Let there be light: and there was light.
4. And God saw the light, that *it was* good: and God divided the light from the darkness.
5. And God called the light Day, and the darkness he called Night. And the evening and the morning were the first day.

CHAPTER TWO

Modern Science and the First Day of Creation

Following the discussion in chapter one, in which we dealt with the time element in the days of creation, we logically proceed to a consideration of the events of the first day in the Mosaic week. This account of God's acts on the first day of creation is found in the first chapter of Genesis, verses 3, 4, and 5.

"And God said, Let there be light: and there was light. And God saw the light, that it was good; and God divided the light from the darkness. And God called the light Day, and the darkness He called Night. And there was evening, there was morning, one day."

The creative event of this single day stands by itself, as no other work that God did is associated with the first day. In order to comprehend the scope of this day's activity, we must carefully and critically read the Mosaic statement. We must carefully note that it is not here stated that this is the primal creation of light, rather this is the first mention of this creature's appearance in the present order of creation. The third verse begins with an imperative positive statement which in the Hebrew text is a mighty compliment to the omnipotence of Deity: "Then said God" (that is to say, the state of things being as just described). This logically refers us to the consideration of the first chapter in this series, and is a reference to the chaos which succeeded the primal state. Ruin, tragedy, and desolation have swept in a chaotic upheaval over the planet that had previously been formed. The earth had become covered with water, shrouded with darkness, wasted, untenanted, and desolate. "Then said God." Re-establishing an ancient order is sometimes a more complicated process than creating a new one. We must not minimize the tremendous scope of this first day in the week of creation which introduces to us once more the creature, light. For the sense of this first verse, there is no exact equivalent in the English translation. The Hebrew text says, "Ye hi or: *wa* ye hi or." The nearest to a literal translation our language will permit is to say, "Light be, and light was;" or even better, "Exist light, then exists light." The whole phrase is one of absolute instantaneity and implies an act that is consummated in the very second of its beginning. Once more we are indebted to Dr. Wilson for this suggestion.

We must also take note of the word here used for light. Our modern word, light, appears again in the English translation of the Bible in the plural in the fourteenth verse: "God said let there be lights in the firmament of Heaven to divide the day from the night." There is, however, a vast difference between the word for light, the creature, in verse three, and the one translated lights in verse fourteen. In verse three the Hebrew word is "or," in verse fourteen the word is "ma-or." This latter word is best translated as luminary; light container; or light holder. We have the same distinction in the Greek where "phos" appears as light, the creature, and "phoster" as the word for a light container. The "ma-or," then, are the great luminaries such as the flaming suns, and even their reflecting satellites called moons, the meteors, and the nebulae; but "or" itself is a creature.

Undoubtedly this light existed in reality from the creation referred to in the first verse of Genesis, "In the beginning God created the heaven:" after that the earth. Since all our light which makes for the division of our daylight from the dark hours comes to us from stellar regions, its creation must be implied in the primal act. This then is the first mention of light in our present order. By some act of omnipotence, God in remaking the original creation and establishing the present order disseminated the darkness so that through its appalling gloom the first gleam of light shines.

Skepticism has criticized this act of the Mosaic record with the contention that we have light manifested on the first day of this creative period while the heavenly bodies which are the light holders do not appear until the fourth day. The contention of semi-knowledge (or absolute ignorance) has been that there could be no light before the creation of the sun. While we will deal extensively with the time of the orb's creation in a following chapter on the fourth day of Genesis, we will pause long enough to say that the criticism is not scientifically tenable. There are many sources of light apart from sunlight itself.

One of the most mysterious of these has been called the aurora borealis. No man who has ever seen the gleaming, crackling, splendor of the northern lights flaming in the Arctic sky, has failed to be impressed with their stupendous grandeur. They are so vivid in view and penetrating in being that they almost strike the ear as a visible sound. If there is a place where light becomes practically audible it is in connection with the aurora borealis. We have heard old men of the north state with earnest conviction that in the quietness of Arctic regions they have heard the northern lights crackle and sing. It was not until recently that we had any real knowledge of the origin of the aurora borealis, but some years ago an amusing explanation was given by an old Negro elevator operator in the city of New York. Due to unusual conditions the aurora was visible for several consecutive evenings, and the whole city was talking about its exceptional splendor. A crowd of scientific and scholarly gentlemen were ascending one of New York's highest buildings in an elevator discussing theories as to the origin of these northern lights. The old elevator operator listened in interest for a few seconds and then interrupted to say, "Gentlemen, I is surprised that such learned people don't know what makes them lights. I kin tell you." Upon being invited to proceed, the interested scholars were delighted to hear him say, "That is just a reflection of the sun and the moon bouncing off the ice on the north pole." The northern lights, however, owe none of their beauty and vivid splendor to either the sun or the moon. It has been demonstrated that a strong electric current passing through nitrogen will glow in a spectrum band comparable to the northern lights, and thus for the first time an indication is given of their possible origin. Here is a light, however, most vivid and unusual, which does not owe its origin to the sun.

Every traveler in tropic seas is familiar with another common light, that is not derived from the sun. On those rare nights when the moon is invisible and the stars are obscured and the equivalent of blackness has settled over the tropic seas, the observer, leaning over the rail of the vessel as the screw churns the water, may see a brilliant gleaming light that transforms the dark depths of the sea into a luminous highway. Men call this light phosphorus, and we know it comes from the glowing bodies of myriads of living creatures. We have seen phosphorus so vivid in semi-tropical waters, that when the agitation was at its height, it was possible to read the figures of a watch by their reflected glow.

Another source of light which owes nothing to the sun is made by that engaging insect, the lightning bug. The lightning bug is almost as much a mystery to the entomologist as is light itself to the physicist. One of the most fascinating spectacles the scientific observer is ever privileged to see is the synchronous flashing of crowds of lightning bugs. Sometimes separated by the breadth of a river, gathered in swarms on opposite sides of the stream, every individual bug will cease his erratic flashing until there have been some minutes of uninterrupted darkness. Then without any signal that human ingenuity can detect, one group will suddenly flash in timed harmony; to be greeted by a similar response from the other swarm. It is impossible at present to say by what mechanism the light of the firefly is controlled. It is impossible to say what is the source of his glow, but we know it does not come from the sun. It is perhaps amusing to comment in passing that while physicists have been searching almost fifty years for a source of light without heat, the lightning bug possesses that secret. In the tail of the lightning bug is the solution of a problem that has so far baffled the wisest physicists of the 20th century!

Another source of light that is not derived from the sun, is the radio active glow that comes from those particles which Sir Oliver Lodge defines as cosmic light. Dr. Lodge contends that if we could get far enough off the surface of the earth, and gaze back at our planet, we would see a ghostly gleam of cosmic light emanating from this ball. In addition to that, there is the fascinating problem of the luminiferous ether which pervades sidereal space. If Moses had contended that light existed before the sun was created, he would thus have been scientifically credible, for there are these sources of light that owe nothing to the sun. However, we wish to reiterate that this work of the first day does not record the act of the creation of the creature, light, but is the first mention of its appearance. We believe the light of the first day was derived from the sun, and consisted of a diffused gleam that penetrated the vapor and the darkness.

Light is a mystery, The best description of light that can be made is to say that it is a physical creature. It is a physical creature because it is susceptible to division into its component parts. We know a little of the nature of light, and we know something of the source of its origin. By means of the marvelous instrument known as the spectroscope, light is made to fit itself into the pigeon holes of a scientific system of filing, so that we can produce from these mystical pigeon holes any kind of ray or beam of light our experiment demands. The reader undoubtedly knows that if a bar of pure iron is heated until it has become incandescent, and the beam from that glowing substance is passed through the prisms of the spectroscope, upon the graph will appear a certain light band which is never any different, if it comes from glowing iron. Now wherever that particular band appears in the spectroscopic analysis of light, we know that iron is the element that emitted it. Again, if copper is the heated element the rays passing through the prism of the spectroscope will follow a path altogether different from that taken by the light of the heated iron. Sodium has a light path individual to itself, and every other metal or element known in physics which can be made incandescent will leave a path that testifies to its individuality. These paths never become confused and were we to amalgamate five or ten or two dozen metals and heat this mass to incandescence, that light upon reaching the spectroscope would give an invariable record of the elements by which it was emitted. We thus say that since light is divisible into its original components it is a creature.

We contend for this same thought by the statement that the speed of light can be measured. We know how fast it travels, and if it dallies on its way there is a method of checking the time spent in side issues. At a rate of one hundred and eighty-six thousand miles a second, light journeys unimpeded through the ether of space. Seven and one-half times around the earth in a second of time is the speed at which light journeys, and because it always keeps to its schedule it has become the astronomical yardstick by which we measure the unthinkable depths of the sidereal skies.

Light is physical, not only to the extent it can be analyzed and measured, but a ray of light may be bent or distorted until it is as crooked as a corkscrew. It may be induced to follow a path, or any geometrical pattern the experimenter desires. It can be bounced off a polished surface and it can also be turned into sound.

While we contend that light is a physical creature it nevertheless has what may be called a spiritual nature. One of the many marvelous phenomena of light is the fact that it can be passed through a physical substance as hard as rock with its speed unimpaired, and its nature unchanged. Even though it passes at many thousand times the speed of a bullet through a physical object, light leaves no hole to mark its passage, and the object through which it thus passed is undamaged! Glass, you know, is artificial rock. The same elements that make stone are used by man in his manufacture of glass. Indeed, the glassware of the laboratory is generally called flint glass, and had the American Indians possessed this type of glass they would have chipped it into arrow heads and weapons superior to those of native flint. Man, by his art and device, takes the elements of stone and transforms them into an artificial sheet of rock which he calls glass. Light, flashing through space, passes unimpeded through this physical substance leaving no hole to mark its passage, being unimpaired in the process. When one physical substance can pass through another physical substance leaving both unimpaired, it is certainly related to the spiritual!

A common phenomenon that manifests the spiritual nature of light is the daily occurrence of the photograph. By the ghostly nature of light the perfect replica of a beloved countenance may be eternally engraved on lasting substances. Even when those we love have crossed the river of death, and their faces and forms are seen no more, their presence is definitely with us in many cases because of the perfection of some photograph, which is naught but a reproduction of light. Scenes of beauty and wonder that would long since have faded from our fallible memories are engraved forever by the photographic process and kept for us as long as our eyes are undimmed. To this extent light is spiritual, and some of its phenomena are beyond human understanding.

It is evident that light was created. There is no other explanation for its marvelous and mysterious power. When skeptics contend that the account of Moses is fallible, let them produce for us a better explanation. The consistent explanation of Scripture is that God created light. One of the striking passages of the Scripture that testifies to the creation of light is found in the one hundred and forty-eighth Psalm, verses three, four, and five:

"Praise ye Him, sun and moon: praise Him, all ye stars of light. Praise Him, ye heavens of heavens, ye waters that be above the heavens. Let them praise the name of the Lord: for He commanded, and they were created."

A verse of equal significance is Isaiah forty-five, verse seven, "I form the light, and create darkness; I make peace, and create evil: I the Lord do all these things." This verse has been a source of wonder to many Bible students, particularly because of the statement of God, "I create evil." We must remember, however, that this does not refer to moral evil. All of the evil of the world may be divided into two classes, the moral, and the physical. Isaiah is not contending that God is the author of lechery, uncleanness, filth, and degeneration. Those are moral evils. We must not forget, however, that when there is danger of collapse in the moral universe, God sends His physical warning. Physical evil may be defined as flood, famine, earthquake, pestilence, and those tremendous cosmic upheavals that shake men off their false foundation of sinful security, and cast them back into dependence upon God. So then, the evil of which God is the author has for its end, good, and it is evil only to the creature who has sinned against God and turned away from Him. The paragraph, however, contains the very definite and specific contention that God Almighty has literally formed, that is to say, *shaped* the light.

Again in Jeremiah 31:35 this same contention appears, "Thus saith the Lord, *Which giveth the sun for a light by day, and the ordinances of the moon and the stars for a light by night,* Which divideth the sea when the waves thereof roar; the Lord of Hosts is His name."

Perhaps the most striking summary of the Scriptural teaching on this subject would be found in II Corinthians 5:6, "For God, *Who commanded the light to shine out of darkness,* hath shined in our hearts, to give the light of the knowledge of the glory of God in the face of Jesus Christ." It is indeed God who has caused light to shine through darkness.

The nature of light is evident from the Mosaic statement, "And God saw the light that it was good." This is a positive assertion that allows no negation, but is susceptible of proof at every angle of inspection. The light is good because it is absolutely pure. Every other physical thing is subject to some adulteration, but it is utterly impossible to conceive of dirty light. So supernal is the character of light in its purity, that it is used variously in the Scripture to bring to the finite conception of man some understanding of the infinite nature of God. Thus we see that God is light. That is to say, one of the attributes of Deity consists of the radiant purity which is associated with light.

Light is good because it is the most useful creature in all God's creation. It is most useful because it makes everything else visible. It is absolutely essential to the enjoyment of every comfort that makes the life of men delightful. Of what use would be the varying terrain upon which we dwell if mountain and plain, river and sea, blossom and bud alike were shrouded with eternal darkness? Of what use the marvelous libraries that man has devised, stored with the treasures of intellect from every age and tongue, if there were no light to make their pages visible? Of what use for heroic men to strain their splendid muscles in athletic competition if they were alike invisible to their opponent and the crowd of spectators who gathered to enjoy the games. Even the fair faces that constitute the hallowed circle of the place we call home, would be forever strange to our comprehension if light did not make it possible to see their varying expressions. Light then is good because it makes all things else visible.

Again, it is good because it makes life possible. If we were under the necessity of groping our way through darkness so impenetrable that the strongest gleam could make no impact thereon, how dismal and gloomy our lives would be. No mechanical inventions to make life pleasant and easy, no artistic achievements to add to our culture and wealth of knowledge. It may truly be said that human achievement is possible only because of this creature called light. Light is good, for if there were no light the world of botany would be impossible. The verdant creatures which grace the surface of the earth have been created to live in light. No one who has ever seen the sickly color of some plant that has struggled for life in semi-darkness can fail to miss the contrast between the green thing which grew in the sunshine, and the pale travesty which grew in the shade.

If there were no light there would be no biology; and the amazing thing is, that light must be exactly as it is to allow life to continue the way we understand it. The biologist is familiar with the marvelous order of life called infusoria. These are tiny microscopic creatures called animalcules, which live in teeming myriads in drops of water. If hay or straw, lettuce, or other vegetation is immersed in water long enough, that water is found to be thronging with these tiny living creatures. They are perfect in their design, they fill their life cycle as do the microscopic animals, and their purpose and function in life is to reproduce their kind. Now these minute creatures, being bred with tremendous rapidity, are the subject of many experiments in biology, as they are the simplest forms of mobile cells with which we may deal.

These infusoria prosper and increase in ordinary light. But when we ascend into the realm of the ultra-violet, that light of such speed and potency as to be invisible to the human eye, we find that these small creatures may be slain by the millions in three-tenths of a second exposure to the power of that ultra-violet ray. There are others of these infusoria that live in the dark, and light is utterly fatal to them. There are other rays of light that are invisible to the human eye. These rays are called the infra-red, and these come at such long frequencies and low vibrations that the eye will not apprehend them. We have demonstrated in laboratory experiments, however, that even those creatures that live in the dark cannot exist without the type of light that is known as the infra-red. From the smallest infusoria in the category of biology, to the most gigantic of the Cetacea that swims the sea, there is not a living creature that does not need some kind of light, even though it be invisible to the human eye.

God saw that the light was good because it is essential to protection. The ancient contention remains as true today as in the day that it was uttered, "Men love the darkness rather than the light because their deeds are evil." In the broad light of the shining sun men walk in comparative safety, but when night's empire rules the globe, tragedy and death, evil and violence stalk hand in hand. Agreeing with God that light is good, man has illuminated his highways and dwellings with artificial light, that he may enjoy its gracious protection.

Again, light is good because it is essential for instruction. There is *no* knowledge without light, and wherever light is, there is *some* knowledge. It may be objected that the blind possess knowledge, while they live in perpetual darkness, but we must remember that the blind do not have real knowledge, they have a limited understanding. Among my acquaintances there is a family whose one daughter is blind. With the pitiful eagerness to render some service which is common to those who dwell forever in the darkness, she always wishes to do what tasks are possible to her limited powers. Although her progress is slow in the act, she is efficient in drying the dishes, and three times a day she delights to render this service. She never saw a dish, but by the sense of touch she has learned to dry and stack them in their proper places. Her sensitive fingers were long delighted by the smooth surface of the tableware she handled and one day she asked, apparently in idle curiosity, "What color are these dishes?" The co-laborer replied that they were white, and the matter was apparently forgotten.

About a week later a visiting lady in the neighborhood paused to have her gown admired by the entire family. The blind girl sat in the corner and listened to the comments and compliments and descriptions of this frock until her curiosity was aroused, and she said, "What color is it?"

Her mother replied, "It is white, with blue trimmings."

The blind girl said, "I know what white it."

Surprised, they said to her, "What is white?"

She replied, "It is anything that is smooth and hard and feels slick."

This is a perfect illustration of the limited knowledge possessed by those who live in the dark. Again, the blind have partial knowledge only *because those who have the light instructed them.* But light is absolutely essential for instruction. So as God gives us the physical light to make mental learning possible, He also gives us the spiritual light that our souls may be instructed in everlasting life.

God saw that the light was good because it is powerful in the service of man in the science of therapeutics. Many diseases which have hitherto baffled the skill of the physician are yielding themselves to the medicinal powers of light. Some diseases are cured by ultra-violet, some are aided by infra-red, others yield to the power of the actinic ray, and man is just entering on a new day in the therapy of light. All these things are implied, and many more, in the statement that God saw that "the light was good."

Again, light is good because it may be transformed into both sound and energy. The most marvelous instrument of the physical laboratory in the twentieth century is the photo-electric cell. The power of the photo-electric cell makes the fabled Aladdin's lamp as obsolete as the kerosene lantern in an old-fashioned barn! When Aladdin rubbed his lamp the genii appeared, and then translated his orders into action. There is no such old-fashioned delay in the magic of the photo-electric cell. At the speed of light it transforms the commands of man into accomplishments. Pictures speak with every vocal intonation of the person being photographed because of the mysterious power of the photo-electric cell. The same beams of light which are transmitted through the photograph to cast the image in visibility upon the screen, are by the photo-electric cell transformed into waves of sound that strike the ear of the auditor exactly as they came from the lips of the speaker, or the mouth of the instrument that played the music.

On the Pacific coast they had a great demonstration of the power of the electric cell when an airplane circling the landing field in the darkness of night, was able by the vibrations of the sound of its motor to turn on the landing lights and flood the field with the essential element, light, as it descended to the earth.

The miracles performed by the photo-electric cell are almost beyond the layman's comprehension. A scientist equipped his laboratory door with a device that would open and close the door when a certain note was struck. Proving his experiment a success, he then equipped his garage door with a lock in the shape of an iron bar, above which was suspended a strong electro-magnet. Connected in series with the magnet was an electric motor, belted to a system of gears that opened and closed the garage door. The photo-electric cell controlling this apparatus was then tuned to the exact note of the owner's horn. Approaching the closed and locked door from the outside, the operator merely sounds his horn. This exact note having been sounded, the photo-electric cell picks up that sound and, moved by that impulse, turns on the current that energizes the electro-magnet, lifting the iron bar that locks the door. The same impulse starts the electric motor which mechanically opens the door. The operator drives in, and when his car is securely inside, he blows his horn the second time and the photo-electric cell proceeds to close the door and lock it securely behind him.

Light is the great servant of man, and we cannot begin to estimate its possibilities. One summer in a harbor in Maine the fishermen and sailors were amazed to see a magnificent steam yacht set sail from the pier without a living soul on board. A system of electric cells and electrically controlled devices had been installed to perform this experiment. From a shore station impulses were transmitted to the faithful cell that started machinery and steered the yacht away from the pier. It went out into the middle of the harbor, circled among various sailing and motor craft, zig-zagged back and forth, made a complete turn and returned to the pier. It stopped at the pier, started again and then backed up, all without a physical hand to touch its helm or direct its machinery. (It has been reported that fourteen fishermen ran home and took the pledge!)

A torpedo was launched in a subsequent experiment, controlled by a photo-electric cell. The shore station was able to control the torpedo with such accuracy they changed its direction nine times, aiming it each time at a distant object, and before its power was exhausted, set its helm to circle and return to the base from which it had departed.

Just how good light *is* we are not at present able to say, for our knowledge of this mysterious creature is in the kindergarten stage. At least we know enough about it to bow in humble wonder before the God who created this powerful creature, and to testify with Moses that "it is good."

Modern science also agrees with Moses that God "divided the light from the darkness." That is a peculiar phrase in the Hebrew text which states that God divided, or separated, the light from the darkness. In a very definite sense of the word, darkness is invisible light, and light is darkness made visible. That sentence sounds complicated and contradictory, but it is a fact that darkness is as visible as light to eyes that are equipped and attuned to perceive. A moving picture was recently exhibited that was made in the laboratory under conditions that the human eye would term absolute darkness. There was no ray of light in the laboratory that was visible to the eye of man. The blackness of the room was so intense that an operator could not see his hand in front of his face, even though it was close enough to his eyes to touch his nose. The camera had been loaded with an especially prepared film made sensitive to infra-red rays. The room, which was dark to the human eye, was flooded with infra-red light, the beams of which were focused on the object being photographed. The camera was set in motion and the shutter opened. The film was then taken from the camera in a developing apartment from which the infra-red rays were filtered, and the film was developed and printed. The audience then had the delightful experience of seeing visibly upon the screen the picture that was taken in "absolute" darkness.

Not only is there light, which is dark to the eye, in the low end of the spectrum, but beyond the upper range of light which our vision can apprehend, darkness really consists of invisible light. In the use of the super-microscope many things have become visible to the bacteriologist and protozoologist which have hitherto been invisible. There are minute creatures in nature whose bodies are pervious to light. They may be termed absolutely transparent. Light passes through their bodies so freely they cast no shadow and thus are invisible to the human vision. We have learned, however, that when the invisible rays of the ultra-violet are the source of illumination for the specimen containing these creatures, their bodies are opaque, or impervious to this degree of light. When the beam of the ultra-violet strikes their bodies, with magical, startling suddenness they leap into visibility in the vision of the observer.

What an amazing thing it is that man can create an eye that will enable him to see in the darkness things that are invisible to his unaided optic organ. As nearly God-like as any achievement man has attained is this remarkable power to make the darkness visible. This is intelligence almost supernatural. This is God-like; only a creature made in His image and likeness would have the ineffable power of reviewing the mysterious works of God and paralleling them to this extent. No beast that roams the field, and progeny of the animal kingdom could ever, by any stretch of imagination, ascend to the height where such creative ingenuity became his possession!

To set this matter clearly before us, let us see that visible or divided light consists of those visible emanations of force that go from red to violet. No man can say why these colors, from red to violet, should be visible and the rest invisible. The only answer is, "It pleased God thus to divide the light from the darkness." The Almighty created the eye of the human being to embrace only that section of the spectrum that is composed of the red to violet keys. We can, however, see the mechanics of this division. Light is a wave of material matter vibrating through space. The same may be said of sound. It is also true of color. There is no such thing as red, or green, blue or brown, in the literal sense of a chemical difference. Colors are merely rays of light material traveling at a different vibration, or a different speed. As an instance, if these waves of material matter vibrating through space are so long as to number thirty-seven thousand six hundred and forty to an inch, and if they come at such frequency as to number four hundred fifty-eight thousand billions a second, they will strike the eye as red. Red then is a light wave arriving on a certain frequency and length of vibration. On the other hand, if this wave of light is shortened until there are fifty-one thousand one hundred and ten to the inch and their frequency is increased so that they arrive at the speed of six thousand two hundred and twenty-two thousand billion a second, they strike the eye with the illusion of blue. Color consists of the rejection, by a physical property, of the light rays whose frequency gives the illusion of the color discarded! As an instance, a red rose may contain in its petals those chemical elements that absorb all the light rays except red. As the blossom rejects the red rays, they are visible to the human eye and we see the rose as red or the rose petals may absorb the complimentary rays, which in this case would be blue-green, thus producing the phenomenon of "red." The fact of the matter is the rose is *every color except red*, the rejected color being the only one visible to the human eye. In botany there is a chemical substance called chlorophyl, which is found in all the green growing things. Chlorophyl has a chemical basis which perfectly reflects the light rays on the green frequency. Other chemicals also have this property, and when wood is painted with a pigment containing this property, or when the vegetation consists of this property, all the light rays will be absorbed except the green. Green grass then is really *not* green. Its power to reflect the green frequency gives it the appearance of color. But truly and literally in physics all color is the same. *It is just light divided differently*. God divided the light from darkness, and thus the human eye cannot see all light. He then divided the light into frequencies that appear as color to brighten the world in which we live. There is no other possible explanation to satisfy the inquiring mind as to why light is thus divided; it is divided so that some of it strikes the eye and some strikes the ear. Light is visible sound, and sound is audible light. If a ray of light speeding on any frequency that makes color can have that frequency changed either higher or lower, the color phenomenon changes also. If those rays of light that make color are slowed down sufficiently they lose their visibility, but strike upon the ear as a high, clear sound. The slower their progress and the lower their frequency, the deeper their tonal value. The difference between a high note of a clear soprano and a deep note of a rumbling bass is only a difference of frequency. If our ears were tuned to receive them we would hear a different tonal value to every light ray, and every "color" in the spectrum. Some light has been divided on a plan to greet the ear, and some to greet the eye.

We note again that after creation, light, like all the other creatures of God, remains under His direct control. In the tenth chapter of Exodus we have the account of the marvelous plagues God visited on Egypt to accomplish the redemption of His people and the conversion of the Egyptians. In verses 21 to 23 we read, "And the Lord said unto Moses, Stretch out thine hand toward heaven, that there may be darkness over the land of Egypt, even darkness which may be felt. And Moses stretched forth his hand toward heaven; and there was a thick darkness in all the land of Egypt three days. They saw not one another, neither rose any from his place for three days; but all the children of Israel had light in their dwellings." Two things we note in this paragraph; that the darkness was impenetrable, no artificial light would shine through it, and that it was so thick as to be *felt*. But while the Egyptians for three days were not able to arise from their beds because of the darkness, the children of Israel had light in their dwellings!

We understand of course that we must not study Genesis from the viewpoint of science alone. There is only one reason why we thus approach our subject and that is because infidelity has adopted the disguise of physical science. We seek only to show that the ancient writings of the man Moses must have been inspired by the Holy Spirit, for certainly no man in the middle of the seventeenth century before Christ could have known these marvelous things that are contained in the first chapter of Genesis. To meet the need of those who doubt, to answer the objections of the infidel, and to set forth from a new angle the undimmed lustre of God's invariable Word, we thus approach this subject in answer to the challenge of infidelity. We desire to conclude this paper, however, with the marvelous Scriptural applications and meanings of the creature that is light.

In the Old Testament as well as in the New, we find that light is given as a symbol or picture of God. Indeed, its very definite language says that light is God and God is light. The 27th Psalm begins with this word, "The Lord is my light." This phrase is found frequently in the Psalms, as for instance in the thirty-sixth Psalm and the ninth verse, "For with Thee is the fountain of life; in Thy light shall we see light." Also Psalm forty-three, verse three, "O send out Thy light and Thy truth: let them lead me; let them bring me unto Thy holy hill, and to Thy tabernacles." Psalm fifty-six, verse thirteen, "For Thou hast delivered my soul from death: wilt not Thou deliver my feet from falling, that I may walk before God in the light of the living?" Again in the eighty-ninth Psalm and the fifteenth verse, "Blessed is the people that know the joyful sound; they shall walk, O Lord, in the light of Thy countenance." There are sixteen other references in the Old Testament, besides these, which refer to light as emanating from God. One of the clearest statements and the most comprehensible of the New Testament is I John 1:5, "This then is the message which we have heard of Him and declare unto you, that God is light, and in Him is no darkness at all." These evidence the fact that in some intangible way the physical creature that is such a mystery to us is associated with the Person of God.

The second Scriptural application of light in the Old Testament and in the New is to the person of the Lord Jesus Christ. We begin our suggested study here with Isaiah, chapter nine, verse two, "The people that walked in darkness have seen a great light; they that dwell in the land of the shadow

of death, upon them hath the light shined." That this light
stands for the person of Jesus Christ we further see from the
tenth chapter and the seventeenth verse, "And the light of
Israel shall be for a fire, and His Holy One for a flame; and it
shall burn and devour his thorns and his briars in one day."
After that also, we note these references, Isaiah, chapter forty-
two, verse six, "I the Lord have called thee in righteousness,
and will hold thine hand, and will keep thee, and give thee
for a covenant of the people, for a light of the Gentiles."
Isaiah, chapter forty-nine, verse six, "And he said, It is a light
thing that thou shouldest be my servant to raise up the tribes
of Jacob, and to restore the preserved of Israel: I will also give
thee for a light to the Gentiles, that thou mayest be my salvation unto the end of the earth." Isaiah, chapter sixty, verse
three, "And the Gentiles shall come to thy light, and kings to
the brightness of thy rising."

In the New Testament the argument is even more conclusive, the prologue to the Gospel of John contains these words,
"In Him was life; and the life was the light of men. And the
light shineth in darkness and the darkness comprehended it
not. There was a man sent from God, whose name was John.
The same came for a witness, to bear witness of the Light, that
all men through Him might believe. He was not that Light,
but was sent to bear witness of that Light. That was the true
Light, which lighteth every man that cometh into the world.
He was in the world, and the world was made by Him, and the
world knew Him not." That this marvelous paragraph applies to the Lord Jesus, He himself testifies in John 8:12,
"Then spake Jesus again unto them, saying, I am the light of
the world; he that followeth Me shall not walk in darkness,
but shall have the light of life." He repeats His testimony in
the ninth chapter and the fifth verse, "As long as I am in the
world, I am the light of the world." In the twelfth chapter
and the forty-sixth verse we read, "I am come a light into

the world, that whosoever believeth on Me should not abide in darkness."

In the Old Testament the Hebrew word used for light, as standing for the person of Jesus, is "or," and in the New Testament the Greek word for "light," as applied to the person of Jesus, is "phos." The significance of this is noted when we see that the characteristic word for the Christian in the New Testament is "phoster," or a light holder. Jesus Christ then is the light and we are the luminaries which contain or shine forth the Light.

The most significant appearance of this word in connection with the Christian is Phil. 2:15, "That ye may be blameless and harmless, the sons of God, without rebuke, in the midst of a crooked and perverse nation, *among whom ye shine as lights in the world.*" This word is comparable to the luminaries of the Old Testament, the Ma-or or the light holders. As definitely as God divided the light from the darkness, so He has separated the believer from the unbeliever. As certainly as the sun adds glory to this world, the disciple of Jesus Christ glorifies the life of the present generation. We are not the light itself, we are the light container, and only as we faithfully shine forth the light of Jesus Christ that is within us are we of value to God and our fellow men.

This study would not be complete without suggesting that there is another word for light in the Greek text of the New Testament which appears in text only twice. This word is "photismos," and we read it in II Corinthians chapter four, verses four to six, "In whom the God of this world hath blinded the minds of them which believe not, lest the light of the glorious Gospel of Christ Who is the image of God, should shine unto them. For we preach not ourselves but Christ Jesus the Lord; and ourselves your servants for Jesus' sake. For God, Who commanded the light to shine out of darkness, hath shined in our hearts, to give the light of the knowledge of the glory of God in the face of Jesus Christ." This word is the basis of our modern term "photograph," and this is the literal implication of the text. The face of Jesus Christ is literally photographed upon our countenance to become our light and our glory, and the face we show to the world should be the illumined countenance; made so by Jesus Christ's presence.

The Word of God concludes its message concerning light with the fifth chapter of Ephesians, verses six to fourteen, "Let no man deceive you with vain words; for because of these things cometh the wrath of God upon the children of disobedience. Be not ye therefore partakers with them. For ye were sometime darkness, but now are ye light in the Lord: walk as children of light: (For the fruit of the Spirit is in all goodness and righteousness and truth:) Proving what is acceptable unto the Lord. And have no fellowship with the unfruitful works of darkness, but rather reprove them. For it is a shame even to speak of those things which are done of them in secret. But all things that are reproved are made manifest by the light; for whatsoever doth make manifest is light. Wherefore He saith, 'Awake thou that sleepest, and arise from the dead, and Christ shall give thee light'."

No greater offer has ever been made to sin-darkened humanity than this concluding prayer, "Awake, thou that sleepest, and arise from the dead, and Christ shall give thee light."

Moses and Meteorology

Genesis Chapter One:

6. And God said, Let there be a firmament in the midst of the waters, and let it divide the waters from the waters.

7. And God made the firmament, and divided the waters which *were* under the firmament from the waters which *were* above the firmament: and it was so.

8. And God called the firmament Heaven. And the evening and the morning were the second day.

CHAPTER THREE

Moses and Meteorology

THE second day in the Mosaic account of creation contains many amazing scientific truths, which Moses could not possibly have known from personal observation. In the very nature of the case, we have a tremendous argument for inspiration in this fact; before certain scientific truths were known to the world of men, aye, ages before the scientific instruments that made their discovery possible were invented, Moses wrote those facts into his record with such clarity that his record has never needed revising! What was the source of his knowledge? It could not have been human wisdom, as no man knew these things to teach them to the writer, Moses. Neither could it have been the result of personal research or observation, as no man at that stage of human culture could have possessed either the technique or the instruments of research that would have been indispensable to such discoveries. So if we reject the theory of inspiration, what other reasonable explanation of this perplexing fact have we?

In the simple language in which his revelation is couched, Moses recounts the entire wonders of this day in these words:

And God said, "Let there be a firmament in the midst of the waters, and let it divide the waters from the waters. And God made the firmament, and divided the waters which were under the firmament from the waters which were above the firmament; and it was so. And God called the firmament Heaven. And the evening and the morning were the second day."

This quotation is taken verbatim from the authorized, or King James Version of the Bible, there being no difference between the wording of this text in that version, and in the American Revised Version, except in the last sentence. The

American Revised Version uses uniformly in the first chapter of Genesis this construction at the end of each day: "And there was evening, and there was morning, a second day." The sense of the two constructions is the same, and each is true to the original Hebrew text.

Two distinct acts are here recorded. First, that the firmament is *made,* then that the waters are *divided* from each other. We will consider the scientific significance of each of these statements in turn. Both statements are equally accurate and significant; the firmament was *made,* it did not just happen to be! And the waters were truly divided from the waters, as there are literally two bodies of water, the terrestial and the atmospheric. Let us consider the firmament and its origin.

The word firmament appears in the entire Old Testament in the original Hebrew manuscript just seventeen times, and nine of those appearances are in the first chapter of Genesis. There is only one Hebrew word so translated in the entire Bible, and that is the word "raqia." It is a word that has provided the modernists with considerable amusement due to their consistent mis-construction of it. Whether this mis-construction and twisting of the meaning is wilful and deliberate, or merely the result of ignorance, the writer cannot say; but since this school makes such brazen claims for the perfection of its own scholarship, we hesitate to say that they are ignorant of this word and its meaning. This leaves the reader to form his own conclusion! The word firmament, the modernist claims, showed that the Hebrews believed that there was a solid, firm sheet of some substantial material spread out between the earth and the sky, and that above this metallic sheet there was stored the rain water. So the Old Testament says in connection with rain, "And the windows of heaven were opened . . ."

This showed, said the modernists, that Moses also believed in this childish idea of the heavens. He also tells us of this firmament, that separates the waters above from the waters below, and it is one of the many ridiculous mistakes in science this writer makes.

Any scholar may safely be challenged to prove this silly contention. No evidence has been produced to show that the ancient Hebrews did so believe. The charge is manufactured to suit the desire of infidelity, and no proof can be advanced to establish this charge that is so often made. The fact of the matter is, that this theory is rather recent, having first been advanced in Medieval times, some twenty-five centuries after the age in which Moses lived!

Now let us examine this word and see how philologically wrong the modernist is in his contention. The word "raqia" comes from a root that means "to spread out," and its literal meaning is a "limitless expanse." Could any more comprehensive definition of the heavens be given than that? Certainly not in human speech. "A limitless expanse" is as accurate a description of the majestic vault of sidereal space as human tongue can frame. There are Hebrew poetic expressions concerning the heavens that may have a suggestion of permanency, or concrete substance, but the word "raqia" is never so used. For instance, in Exodus, the twenty-fourth chapter and the tenth verse, Moses makes a poetical reference to the heavens as "a transparent sapphire" (which is a beautiful figure of speech), but he does not use the word for firmament, which lacks any sense of concrete substance. Again, in the one hundred and fourth Psalm the writer says in the second verse, that God ". . . stretched out the heavens like a curtain." Here again the writer is careful *not* to use the word firmament, as that would be a violation of any possible meaning of the word "raqia." The same thing is seen in Isaiah forty, verse twenty-two, where the heaven is called a curtain, but the word there used is "yediah," not "raqia." To use the word "raqia" here would be an unpardonable violation of the rules of the Hebrew language, as the poetic expression of the prophet implies solidity, and such cannot be conveyed by the word firmament. "Raqia," or firmament, is never used in a poetical reference in the Hebrew text, because *all the possible meanings of the word "raqia" are nebulous,* or intangible.

The firmament here spoken of is inclusive, as we see from the appearances of this word in the first chapter of Genesis. It means the sidereal or starry heavens, as the fourteenth verse of this chapter shows. Here the statement is made that lights (the sun, moon, and stars) were placed in this firmament, so it extends beyond the atmosphere of this earth. But that the word also includes this earth's atmosphere we see in the twentieth verse as the statement is there made that the birds are to fly in the open firmament of the heaven. This firmament, then, includes the atmospheric and the starry heavens, but *not* the heaven that is the place of God's habitation. That is referred to in the Scriptures as the third heaven, and is somewhat apart from, or beyond, the sidereal system that contains the stars. This firmament has been a sore puzzle to men of science, and to explain its amazing mysteries and contradictions, the eminent physicist, Sir Oliver Lodge, postulates the ether of space. This is a firmament indeed; as Lodge says, it is "as rigid as steel, yet so nebulous as to offer no resistance to light speeding through its structure, and to offer no impediment to the concrete bodies that pass at incredible velocities through this spatial ether."

Let us then paraphrase this text of Moses by a trans-literation into English, and we shall see that it then reads, *"Let there be something nebulous and unlimited spread out between the waters to separate the water from the water."* At this statement we are content to let Ignorance laugh; but we will pause to investigate. The reader must know that there is a certain type of mind that finds a peculiar humor in any situation too deep for its understanding, and many so-called "thinkers" have laughed this passage to scorn. The charge is made by this school that the Hebrews believed, or at least Moses taught, that there were two bodies of water, with the "firmament" separating them from each other. This strikes the freethinker and the modernist as too funny for words: yet this is exactly what scientific investigation reveals to be the fact.

But if the Mosaic statement were not so, where would this earth-life exist? For these *are* the two bodies of water, the upper and the lower, and if they were not *separated* nothing could exist except the fish. And as the fish would soon exhaust the supply of oxygen in the lower body of water, it is doubtful if even they could long exist, if the upper body of water was not separated from the lower! The supply of oxygen essential for the support of life, whether animal or human, is in the atmosphere, and without that atmosphere, from which the ocean's supply of oxygen must constantly be replenished, even fish would not be able to survive.

The condition of this globe when the Second Day was ushered in must not be forgotten. It was in an aqueous state entirely, as far as its surface was concerned. The atmosphere was purely a cloud of steamy vapor, that obscured the heavenly bodies like a thick veil. The very rays of the sun themselves were unable to penetrate this depressing mist, and the pale and ghostly gleam of the first day's light was dimmed as the result of that fog. As yet there was no land in sight, but the terrain that was so soon to be covered with a verdant carpet of vegetation was now wrapped in a grim blanket of moisture, which was both liquid and solid. Where the fluid waters did not cover the place that was to be the land, the frozen and stony ice prevailed. The vapor touched and clung to the very face of this watery, frozen waste, and the waters literally merged with the waters.

Now, on this day, in order to provide a space where life could exist on this planet, God "divided the waters from the waters." That is, the vast waste of water was divided into two separate bodies, the upper, and the lower. Of the lower we need not now speak, as it is visible to the human eye, and all accept its presence and its reality because of the evidence of sight. We sail its surface, and fish in its depths. On the floor that contains it we dredge for treasures, and clothed in diving armor we walk in quest of strange adventures. We swim in its invigorating embrace, and by physical reactions we accept the fact that the lower body of water is water indeed.

Somehow, however, we fail to realize that the "upper" body of water is equally as real. In very truth it *is* as real as the ocean itself. In fact, the firmament contains a veritable ocean in suspension, and if its contents suddenly decided to join the lower ocean from whence it came in creation's week, devastation and the utter destruction of man and all his works would be the inevitable result.

This ocean of the upper waters contains waves and bounding billows, that are tossed about into mighty floods by currents, called winds. Like the ocean beneath, it has tides which ebb and flow in irresistible power, governed by the same forces and powers that make possible the tides of the sea. In that upper ocean we have now learned to navigate, and our stellar ships must be able to float on its aqueous content, as our ocean liners and our submarine vessels sail on and under the sea. In that upper ocean birds "swim" through the atmospheric waters as the fish swim in the sea, and man has at last learned their art. But our atmospheric ships must be constructed in accordance with the laws of the fluid element they are designed to navigate, and when for some reason or other there is insufficient moisture in that atmosphere these ships have heavy weather, and often as not cannot leave the ground. If in the course of an aerial voyage the celestial mariner is shipwrecked, he will sink to the bottom of that upper body of water until he lands with a crash. Unless he has had the wisdom to provide himself with a "life preserver" in the shape of a parachute he may then expect to perish. What difference is there between the parachute of the aviator and the life preserver of the sailor, except a matter of degree? Each is designed to enable the shipwrecked man to float in the particular "sea" he may be navigating.

Every peculiar characteristic of the ocean that rests on the surface of the earth may be paralleled in the upper sea that is held in place by the construction of the firmament. In the salt water of the ocean we find types of life that could not exist anywhere else; so in the waters of the atmosphere we have thousands of species and varieties which are suited to that environment and to that one alone.

The ocean has a specific weight and pressure. This pressure increases with the depth, until the bottom is reached. In the depths of the ocean there dwell strange creatures which are designed to withstand the degree of pressure there encountered, and if these creatures are caught and brought up to the surface they literally explode when that pressure is relieved. A moment's consideration will show why this occurs. Their muscular structure is graduated to the weight of the pressure at the normal depth where they reside, and this is a marvel of engineering skill. If the pressure they must resist is, let us say, ten thousand pounds per square foot, their muscles are built to thrust at the rate of ten thousand pounds per square foot, and compensation is established. Now, if that pressure is suddenly relieved by bringing the creature forcibly to the surface, where the pressure is only twenty-one hundred pounds to the square foot, the muscles continue to push against this minimum pressure with their established force and the result is that the creature is literally torn asunder by his own muscular power.

We note exactly the same condition in the upper body of water, that we see prevailing in the lower ocean. There is a certain weight or pressure there also, and it is heaviest on the bottom of this atmospheric sea, which is, of course, sea level. At this level we have an atmospheric pressure of about fourteen pounds and nine ounces per square inch. This means that every square foot of surface at sea-level is under a pressure of about twenty-one hundred pounds. So the surface of the earth must bear a constant weight of approximately fifty-eight billion, six hundred and eleven million, five hundred forty-eight thousand pounds per square mile! To make it easier to grasp, let us write it this way: 58, 611, 548, 000 pounds per square mile. And every creature that lives on the face of the earth must be so constructed as to resist this pressure constantly. Even the tiny gauzy insects of myriad hues must resist with their tiny bodies this pressure of almost fifteen pounds per square inch. Some of these living creatures have bodies that are a miracle of design, and that awaken wonder and awe in the mind of the investigator who studies their perfect structures.

Let us apply this pressure to man. We think that a man who can lift with ease two hundred pounds is strong, and we know that if a ton of metal was suddenly dumped on the back of the strongest and mightiest man this earth contains he would sink beneath that weight, crushed, never to rise again. *Yet the average man must be able to bear constantly, both day and night, an atmospheric pressure of over fourteen tons at sea level.* This is unthinkable; the mind refuses to grasp a proposition so bizarre. Yet this is literally and scientifically true: at the sea-level pressure of nearly fifteen pounds per square inch a man of the average size (and a woman as well) must be constructed to carry a pressure of fourteen tons.

This compensation is accomplished automatically by the musculature of the human structure, which was all carefully thought out and planned by the Creator in the first creation of the race. This same compensation was also accomplished by creative genius in the origination of every type of life that lives on the earth, under it, or above it. This is one of the marvels of creation, and argues convincingly to the thinking mind, that there must have been a Cause for every effect, or for the Fact of *God* in Creation.

For the reason, then, that we are constructed to withstand a sea-level pressure, when we climb a high mountain, or with our airships navigate too near the surface of this aerial ocean, headache, dizziness and distress result. If we go high enough we become unconscious, as the internal pressure of our muscles begins to tear us apart. For just like the fish that normally lives at a low level, if we are taken up where pressure ceases, we too will destroy ourselves by our own power. Just as the eyes of a deep water cod are the first to pop out when we bring it up to the top of the ocean, so our heads feel that frightful effect of the reduction of the sea-level pressure before any other part of the structure suffers, and we have the familiar phenomenon that every mountain climber has experienced.

Like the oceanic crustacea, we live on the floor of a sea! Down on the bottom of the ocean the crabs, the lobsters, and shell-fish of many varieties happily live their life cycle; in an environment to which they are fitted. So do we; for we are in residence, like crustacea, on the "bottom" of the firmamental sea.

How did Moses know this? Ages before men of science learned these facts they were recorded in fidelity to their unfailing truth in this, the first book of Moses. *Did Moses know these facts,* or did he speak by inspiration when he wrote these words? Job apparently knew this also, else he too spoke by the power of the Spirit of God when he said, that God maketh "the *weight* for the winds, and weigheth the waters by measure." Settle this query to your own satisfaction, but at any rate confess that Moses was in harmony with modern science when he said the firmament was established to separate the waters above from the waters below.

The composition of this upper sea further bears out the accuracy of Moses. While there are several minor elements in the atmosphere, its main ingredients are two, nitrogen and oxygen. The proportion is:

Nitrogen	79 parts
Oxygen	21 parts

to every 100 parts of atmosphere.

This proportion is constant and consistent, whether at sea level or on the tops of the very highest mountains. Descend as deep into the heart of the earth as a natural cave or a mine dug by man will allow you to penetrate, and there you will find the atmosphere has this established proportion of oxygen and nitrogen. Fly as high as an airship can carry you, and as far as the atmosphere exists this proportion never varies. At the north pole or at the south, in the fertile tropics or the arid desert, this ratio is constant and unchanging. This is an amazing evidence of design. Suppose there was a little more or less of either element in the atmosphere; would it really matter? Indeed, this is apparently the one possible proportion that will support life as we know it now.

If there were too much nitrogen in the atmosphere, the result would be a lethargic slowing down of the processes of the human body that would ultimately produce death. Increase the oxygen, on the other hand, and the human pulse would race at such a feverish rate that life would quickly cease. The processes of the cell structure would be so sped up that the heart would soon break, and the very structure of the tissue would be consumed by the excess of oxygen. If the proportion of the atmosphere were so changed that we had two parts of nitrogen to one of oxygen, and some electrical action should cause these elements to combine, the earth might soon be peopled with raving maniacs, whose empty and uncontrolled laughter would make a bedlam of the entire globe. N_2O is, as you well know, the famous "laughing gas," or nitrous oxide which the dentist uses upon occasion. Can we imagine a human race that suddenly began to breathe that mixture for their normal atmosphere!

Change the proportion of the atmosphere until its two chief elements were balanced, and we have N_2O_2 or nitric oxide. Step into the laboratory for a few minutes and get a whiff of this gas and note the result; after you recover of course, — for the result will be contraction of the glottis that will leave you choked and breathless for some time after. If *this* were the proportion of the atmosphere, and combustion should ensue we could not breathe, as the glottis would remain contracted and the lungs could not function. Even though this imaginary combination should never occur, it still remains true that present orders of life are utterly dependent upon the continuance of the present proportion of oxygen and nitrogen in the atmosphere. To make a long story short, let us note that there are an unlimited number of mathematical proportions that are possible here, and we are amazed that Creation "happened" to hit upon the one possible one that would support life as it now is! Was this an accident? Did "a fortuitous combination of accidental circumstances" arrange this? The "accidents" that occur in chemistry usually result in explosions! Especially where these two tricky elements are concerned.

Nor must we miss the significance of the weights of these two chief ingredients of the atmosphere. This is important, for when we breathe the atmosphere into our lungs the system uses up chiefly the oxygen content and the nitrogen is exhaled with the exhausted breath. Since man, and the vast animal world as well, are exhaling vast quantities of exhausted atmosphere with every breath, whether sleeping or waking, it is essential that some provision be made to care for the nitrogen thus released into the atmosphere, right on the level where it would naturally be inhaled back into the lungs that had just exhaled it. This would soon be fatal to the individual who did much breathing in any one spot! Since the normal rate of respiration is about twenty times a minute, in the course of twenty-four hours the exhausted exhalations of one pair of lungs will reach twenty-eight thousand eight hundred and spill into the area occupied by that individual four hundred fifty cubic feet of atmosphere, from which the oxygen content has been seriously depleted. Increase this amount by the number of individuals, human and animal, in any restricted space, and see the necessity of sleeping with windows open for replenishment of the atmosphere!

In considering these facts, we see at a glance that if the nitrogen were heavier than the oxygen, the earth would soon be blanketed with a thick covering of nitrogen lying like a cloud of poison-gas such as filled the dug-outs in the last war in Europe. Every room of human habitation, every barn or stall occupied by any animal, indeed, the very "open air" itself would be a death-trap very soon, if the oxygen in the air were lighter than the nitrogen. But such is not the case. Nitrogen weighs less than oxygen, the difference being .078 grams per litre, and thus it rises above the heavier element, oxygen. Thus, also, life is preserved on the face of the earth. A small part of this element, oxygen, remains in the exhaled breath, but the overwhelming preponderance of each exhalation is nitrogen. In its free state it means death to the mammal, so God in His creative wisdom made it so that it ascends immediately after it leaves the nostrils. Thus on a frosty morning we see the breath *ascending,* and witness this law in operation.

Can any intelligent reasoner say that this is the result of accidental coincidence? The very nature of the elements of the atmosphere cries out against this idea; intelligence is seen in fixing the weight of nitrogen below that of oxygen so that the nitrogen, released from its association with the oxygen, ascends like a balloon to the upper regions, where the atmospheric disturbances cause it to associate once more with its fellow of the atmosphere, and gradually return to the lower strata to serve man and nature.

This firmament, then, is under the constant control of the iron hand of God, its Creator. If the atmosphere should slip out of control, chaos would quickly result. Nitrogen, for instance, is the basic ingredient of practically every explosive used in man's warfare. The reason why the German government was able to enter the great war with such confidence was because her scientists had perfected a method of extracting the nitrogen from the atmosphere and transforming it into gunpowder! The earliest formulas for gunpowder were generally based on the presence of one atom of nitrogen in combination with two atoms of oxygen (NO_2) which formed the "nitro group." Smokeless powder, an improvement on this older type, was derived by taking the nitro group out of the nitrate by means of sulphuric acid. A simple but powerful form of this order is the common explosive, nitroglycerin, which is formed by glycerine, nitric acid and sulphuric acid.

If cellulose is used in place of glycerine, the result is nitrocellulose, a powerful gunpowder used by the army, especially in major-caliber artillery. By means of a strong electric current, the nitrogen atom is forced to combine with two oxygen atoms, resulting in a brown, vile-smelling gas. This gas (NO_2) is dissolved in water, oxidized, and thus becomes nitric acid. This amazing result is produced by forcing a stream of ordinary atmosphere over a violent electric arc! So that when the lightning flashes through the firmament above, the result is, when followed by rain, the basic ingredient of a powerful explosive!

Nitroglycerin is a liquid, and must be converted into a solid to be a practicable and useful explosive. In the case of dynamite, this is done by soaking sawdust in the nitroglycerin in percentages that vary with the powers produced, and then moulding it in paper tubes into the familiar "sticks." But the nitro-cellulose (commonly called "guncotton") is a fluffy solid, and should be saturated with liquid to make it most economical. So the nitro-cellulose is soaked in the nitroglycerin, and man is provided with the amazing and even appalling power called "cordite" which has made war so horrible a thing. And all this is because of the presence in the atmosphere of nitrogen! If *that* element ever gets out of control, good-bye Planet Earth!

The other main ingredient of the atmosphere, oxygen, is no less fierce when *it* goes on a rampage. There is no possibility of combustion without oxygen. Nothing can burn without its aid. Therefore when explosives are compounded some chemical formation must be induced that will associate the oxygen with the explosive basis, or even such a thing as nitroglycerin would fail to burn. That is why you have a carburetor on your automobile engine; gasoline cannot burn without oxygen. So the carburetor functions to inject a stream of air with the gasoline, and thus with oxygen's aid combustion occurs in the firing chamber of the cylinder head of the car's engine.

In the natural, or atmospheric condition, this element is a gentle and gracious thing, making life possible in this environment. In the hospital it is used to soothe pain and prolong life, and the mild and helpful nature of oxygen has made us lose sight of the fact that it might be a veritable demon of destruction. In conjunction with acetylene, it is able to eat a hole through the most powerful steel which science can construct. If the oxygen in the atmosphere should ever be released to work its will it has the power to melt the living rocks, consume our skyscrapers as a blast-oven would destroy tissue paper, and utterly obliterate the entire works of man.

We sometimes wonder if this is what Peter had in mind when he said, "But the day of the Lord shall come as a thief in the night, in which the heavens shall pass away with a great noise, and *the elements shall melt with fervent heat;* the earth also and the works that are therein shall be burned up." "Looking for and hastening unto the coming of the day of God, wherein the heavens being on fire shall be dissolved, and the elements shall melt with fervent heat." These are highly significant words in the light of the fact that the oxygen in the atmosphere could really melt the very earth, if its appalling power were turned to destruction. Happily, however, the firmament is ruled with an iron hand.

All these things are marvelous as we consider the structure of the firmament, but the most amazing fact in this whole suggestive study is not the structure, but *the function of the firmament*.

Let us first state the problem: How are we continually to water the tops of the highest mountains and the upland plains? Nothing can grow without water, and if the earth is to produce its carpet of green, which in turn will provide food and sustain the life of man and beast and bird, how are we to water the highlands that lie so far above the ocean level? The solution lies in the Mosaic statement; by dividing the waters from the waters, and causing the upper waters in the firmament to be available for the thirsty land. The technique of this solution is seen in the phenomena that men call evaporation and precipitation.

In order that we may clearly comprehend the wonder of this solution, let us re-state our problem, dividing it into its various parts. The problem resolves itself into three divisions:

a. There is plenty of water in the ocean, but it must be transported.

b. The ocean water contains salt, which is fatal to plant life. Therefore, the water must be purified.

c. The great weight of the water, which is eight hundred times that of the atmosphere, must be overcome.

Thus we see that the problem is even more complicated than at first appears. So we will consider the solution of this problem in the reverse order in which we stated its three divisions.

The third factor, that of the weight of the water, is solved by heat. The law of nature is that heat expands an object; cold contracts it. Water is subject to marvelous expansions, steam being water that is expanded sixteen hundred times its original volume! The atmosphere is thus able to hold an unbelievable quantity of water, limited largely by the temperature of the atmosphere. In a room sixty feet each way, where the temperature is sixty degrees Fahrenheit, the atmosphere can easily sustain two hundred and fifty-two pounds of water! The expanding power of water is almost unbelievable. If all the fog necessary to blanket the entire harbor of New York with a mist too thick for navigation, were reduced to water again, that amount of fog would scarcely give water enough to fill a five-gallon bucket to the brim!

Now, we saw that water is about eight hundred times the weight of the atmosphere. The effect of solar heat, as the sun shines hour after hour, is to expand the water it affects to nine hundred times its normal bulk. That makes this resulting "vapor" one-eighth lighter than the atmosphere, so it ascends quickly and naturally. The vapor gathers itself into great bodies called clouds, which may in some cases be many, many hundreds, nay, even thousands of feet thick. Cloud colonies may also cover many square miles of the atmosphere in extent. How few of us realize that the firmament is so extensive that it could hold in suspension several times the amount of all the water in all the oceans on the face of the earth! Here, then, is the solution of division c. of our problem: the weight is overcome by solar heat.

The second section of the problem is solved the same way. The impurities in the water are all solids, and while they also are subject to expansion by heat, they do not volatilize, or become vapor, except at high temperatures far above that which the sun is capable of causing at its present distance. So, when the vapors rise in response to the sun's warm influence only the water is taken up. All the solids remain in the sea, so the water is purified. This accounts for the condition of the rain water that housewives call "soft," and which makes it so pleasing to them in certain of their duties.

With these two problems solved, there still remains the most difficult one, that of transportation. When all this has taken place, the clouds are right above the ocean from which they were formed, and if precipitation now results, the water will fall right back into the sea, and the land will be no whit benefited. Here is where the "tides" and "currents" of the upper ocean function, and the atmospheric streams we call winds sweep the clouds irresistibly off and bear them to the far-distant lands. They are thus delivered, with their precious freight of water, where they are most needed.

Now another phase of the problem enters into our study. These clouds are formed of what we might call "water dust," and if they are light enough to float, will stay up indefinitely. How are we to bring the water down? Evaporation solved our problem by expansion through heat: now precipitation, or the actual delivery of the water to the thirsty land, is to be made possible by the opposite process, loss of heat, resulting in contraction. So, as the clouds lose their heat, being cooled by the icy breath of the mountain peaks, or the cold, clammy air that rises from the highlands below them, the vapor condenses back to its natural state and the water begins to fall, in the shape of rain.

We must note, however, that this loss of heat must be gradual. Many thousand tons of water are suspended in the fleecy blanket of clouds, and if those clouds lost their heat all at once, this water would drop on the terrain beneath with devastating force and bring destruction instead of blessing. We occasionally see such a condition in what we refer to as a cloud-burst; which is simply the result of the sudden loss of too much heat by some passing cloud. Giant trees are beaten to the earth, houses are crushed like straw, and floods pour down the mountain canyons to devastate towns in the valley: all because a cloud cooled off too quickly! This process must be under some powerful control.

So the loss of water by a cloud is governed in unvarying ratio by a mathematical rule which proportions the precipitation, on a table that is graded to the loss of heat elements. So a cloud floating in a current of air that has a temperature of eighty degrees Fahrenheit will lose one-fourth of its load if the temperature is reduced nine degrees. If it then loses twelve more degrees of heat, that cloud will spill one-third of its remaining load, so a loss of twenty-one degrees of heat results in the precipitation of half the water content of that particular cloud. This scale of loss by reduction of heat elements is so planned as to make the rain descend in gentle showers under certain conditions, and as a vigorous downpour under other conditions. But the land is watered, from the mountain tops to the fertile plains.

Our friends the materialists object to the citation of this as evidence of the presence of God in creation and nature. "All this is purely mechanical," says the materialist, "it is simply the result of a natural law." To prove this contention, he cites a common phenomenon: a certain proportion of the clouds spills the water back into the sea, and it never reaches the land! Thus he seeks to prove that there is no intelligence in the functioning of the firmament!

We, of course, are willing to accept this correction, and admit that this process is mechanical. Let us make of it an equation, as follows:

Mechanics equals Machine. Machine equals Inventor. Q.E.D.! That is all we hoped to demonstrate; Intelligence is behind the whole process. There is no law, natural or otherwise, without a legislative body or Being, we must repeat. There are no machines without inventors, and mechanics cannot be separated from the intelligence that produced them.

There is a good and sufficient reason why some of the rain falls back into the sea. It serves a useful purpose in so doing. Everybody who owns a gold fish in a bowl knows that reason! As the oxygen in the water is used up by the fish, it must be replenished. If the aquarium does not contain those plants that renew the oxygen content in the water, the owner of the bowl renews the oxygen by the simple process of dipping up the water in a container, and pouring it back into the bowl from some height. This process of aeration puts the vital element back into the bowl, and that is just what the rain does when it falls back into the sea.

Let the intelligent marvel at this: annually, the rivers on the face of the planet Earth pour into the oceans one hundred and eighty-six thousand, two hundred and forty *cubic miles* of water. All this vast amount must be returned to the land every year, else the water supply of the land will soon be inadequate. Now, if this amount of water was all sent back at once, it would cover the entire earth to a depth of three feet. But Divine Wisdom, in the establishment of the functions of nature, ordained that the gentle and blessed rain should replenish the water supply on a more kindly basis than that.

No wonder the man of God in Ecclesiastes marveled when he said, "All the rivers run into the sea, yet the sea is not full. Unto the place whither the rivers came, thither they return again." Did he also speak by inspiration?

We call ourselves intelligent, who live in cities and plan our own affairs, because at tremendous cost we provide ourselves with water. And it *is* at tremendous cost. One Pacific coast city has invested over two hundred and fifty million dollars in her water works and equipment, and it costs in addition nearly forty million dollars a year to keep the supply running. Other cities pay even more than that: yet the wilderness gets it for nothing! There is thus an element of humor in God's controversy with Job, when in the thirty-eighth chapter of that book it is recorded that the Creator says to the patriarch, "Who causes it to rain on the wilderness and the desert places, *where no man is?* Who waters the grass there that the animals may eat?" It seems as though God is smiling at Job, and says, "You fellows can run your *cities* fairly well, but who is the Gardener of the *wilderness?*"

Because the firmament does carry a body of water which is really an ocean, many things are possible. When the water is deposited on the mountain peaks, it instantly starts to seek its natural level, the sea, and it never rests content until it gets there. So we harness it, in passing, to the wheels that turn the grindstone in the mill, to the lathe of the shop, or the giant saw that bites its way through the fallen tree and converts it into lumber; or we guide it through mighty tubes and force it to generate the electric current that operates our street cars, or lights our homes. All the amazing wonders of power wrought by the hydraulic engineer are possible only because of this: God divided the waters from the waters, and established an ocean in the firmament above.

"So God divided the waters from the waters," wrote Moses. How easy to say; how difficult to perform! Water is one of the most mysterious elements of the laboratory. It is itself a creature of God.

It is dodging the issue for the rationalist, the atheist, the materialist, and the modernist to say, "All these things you here portray are merely the result of the action of water obeying the laws of nature. Of course the clouds must form when the sun shines on the water: that shows that water is obedient to the natural law which says heat will expand any given object, and cold will contract it." Ah, but, we note that water does not always obey nature's laws! There is a mysterious character about water which makes it a delightful Bolshevik, fascinating in contradictions, that are inherent in its very structure.

It is not an element, as you well know, but is a combination of two elements, hydrogen and oxygen. Both of these are gases, yet when they are combined in the proportion of two atoms of hydrogen to one atom of oxygen they form a fluid which is not a gas, and we call that fluid water. Hydrogen is probably the most inflammable gas known to science. It goes off in combustion with a roar on the slightest excuse. Oxygen, as we saw above, is the element that is responsible for all combustion. Now we combine the two gases, one highly explosive and the other the cause of combustion, and they form a fluid that puts out the fire! This is absolutely unreasonable, but we know it to be the truth, nevertheless.

Again, we note that water obeys the law of contraction by the loss of heat only as far as it seems to please the water molecules to do so. Then they revolt and go their own happy, independent way. Job calls attention to this phenomenon when he states in the thirty-eighth chapter of his manuscript that "The waters are turned into a stone, when the face of the deep is frozen" and pauses to wonder that this "stone" does not sink to the bottom. This is a real problem; why does ice float? It is because it violates that law of contraction by the loss of heat.

When water begins to freeze it starts out to obey this law. Down to the temperature of thirty-eight degrees Fahrenheit, the shivering molecules lose their bulk as they huddle together to keep warm, but at this temperature the loss of size ceases, and from then on, down to the point of freezing, *the water gains all the bulk it lost, plus some thirty per cent more!* So then while cold *does* cause an object to contract, it fails to work out in the case of this delightful rebel, water. What a blessed gift to man this thing called ice is, so long as he keeps it under control!

On the other hand, we see the violation of the opposite law to this one of contraction by this same creature, water. When the ice is melted back into water again, the law that says heat expands an object does not then apply. The ice melts into water, and loses something over a quarter of its bulk as it warms up! What an amazing creature this thing called water is! Drink it in its fluid state, and it brings health and life to the body. Expand its bulk sixteen hundred times, and it will drive the commerce of the nations on land or sea. In that condition, however, it is ready to rend its master, man, at the slightest opportunity, and instead of bringing health and life to his body is ever ready and eager to scald the skin from his frame, and roast him to death! After it has been expanded these sixteen hundred times, it can be condensed back into water again, and turned into a "stone" that floats, and can be crunched between the teeth and made to cool the body in the summer heat. But in this, as in all its many guises, it is ready to destroy man, the master, either by scalding, freezing, or drowning him. It is dangerous to take your eye off water, as you never know what it will do next!

That water is a creature of God we see in the fact that it was under the control of the Lord Jesus when He walked the earth, God Incarnate. First we see His power of control of this creature of nature, when in Cana of Galilee He turned the water into wine. We see it once again manifested when upon the Lake of Galilee the storm threatened to destroy the lives of all who were in the boat. He rebuked the waters, and they grew quiet at His command.

Highly significant is the magnificent figure of speech the Lord used when He used water to symbolize eternal life. Water is indeed the fit symbol of life, as every drop teems with it. Whether it be the salt water of the boundless sea, the alkaline pool in the desert waste, the sweet waters of a babbling brook, or the moisture that is in the plants and the trees; every drop of water is a little world that teems with life. Not only does water contain life, it also prolongs, extends and confers it. It saves life as well, as many can testify who all but perished on the desert sands, and were restored to life by a few drops of this priceless fluid. And the bleaching bones of many a lost creature who failed to find water in time, will add their testimony to this, and also say that water confers and conserves life.

So it is unusually significant that Jesus should say to the woman of Samaria, as they conversed by the well, ". . . Whosoever shall drink of the water that I shall give him shall never thirst, but the water that I shall give him shall be in him a well of water, springing up into everlasting life." And again when at the feast of Tabernacles He stood in the temple and cried: "If any man thirst, let him come unto Me and drink. He that believeth on Me, as the Scripture hath said, From within him shall flow rivers of living water."

It is also interesting to note that water enters the sacred record of God's own Book on its first page and its last. In the very first chapter of the Bible, Moses introduces us to this amazingly mysterious fact of the division of the waters and the establishing of the firmament; the last chapter of the Book contains this further verse: "And the Spirit and the Bride say, 'Come! And . . . let him take the water of life freely.'"

We cannot take that "water of life," however, so long as we deny its source and doubt its value. The man without Christ today is like a dying creature, perishing of thirst by the side of a lake of pure, sweet water, because he will not believe that the water is good to drink!

We come back, in conclusion, to the subject at the head of this chapter, and raise the question, "Did Moses know when he penned these words, that the scientific knowledge of the twentieth century after Christ would vindicate his every statement and claim?" He probably did not know.

How did Moses know these great truths concerning the nature and structure of the marvelous creature, water, so as to write in perfect harmony with modern science? *We do not claim that Moses knew these things; but rather that when he wrote, he wrote by the inspiration of the Holy Spirit, Who guided him.*

The Doxology of the Deep

Genesis Chapter One:

9. And God said, Let the waters under the heaven be gathered together unto one place, and let the dry *land* appear: and it was so.

10. And God called the dry *land* Earth; and the gathering together of the waters called he Seas: and God saw that *it was* good.

11. And God said, Let the earth bring forth grass, the herb yielding seed, *and* the fruit tree yielding fruit after his kind, whose seed *is* in itself, upon the earth: and it was so.

12. And the earth brought forth grass, *and* herb yielding seed after his kind, and the tree yielding fruit, whose seed *was* in itself, after his kind: and God saw that *it was* good.

13. And the evening and the morning were the third day.

CHAPTER FOUR

The Doxology of the Deep

THE most stupendous series of events ever recorded in one paragraph is found in the first chapter of the book of Genesis, verses nine to thirteen. In the thrilling words that face this page we are now reading, the inspired writer records in words so simple that a child can comprehend them, three of the amazing acts of creation.

Three marvelous events, in just one hundred and twenty words, are here recounted in the Divine record. And so clearly are these events thus portrayed that all the libraries of the world cannot more clearly convey this message. Surely the equal of this paragraph is not to be found in any purely *human book;* man does not so write. In simple as well as concise language this tale is told, for in the one hundred and twenty words of this clear-cut statement one hundred of them are words of one syllable! Human wisdom is not thus expressed. Only supernal intelligence can express such mighty deeds in language so simple that a child can grasp it all So well couched is this text in the Hebrew manuscript, that in the American Revised Version of the Bible in the English language, only one word is interpolated by the translators to make the translation faultless, and that is the simple word "and."

On this wondrous day of creation, three events are recorded. The ocean is formed, the dry land appears, and botany is born. Here the Divine cosmogony tells of all these events in one simple paragraph; man has been writing about these events for hundreds of years, and in all that time has never, in clarity, approached this paragraph. Imagine all the books that have been written on botany! Add to that the list which the science of geology has called forth; complete the record with all the writings of oceanography; wander in a daze through the long and weird verbiage of their construction, and then come back and read this paragraph again. This simple statement is certainly superhuman.

In the first chapter we considered the question of the time period in these days of creation, and this is the only occasion so far where the word "day," or "yom," can be stretched to mean an epoch. If the "yoms" or days of creation were geological eras, then we can assume that there was a gradual development, over a period of ages, of this three-fold work of creation. The statement is made that the eternal sea gives up a portion of its area to form the dry land. Now reason may well ask, "Could the resulting saline ooze support vegetation after a twenty-four hour period?" On the other hand, reason may well assume that if ages were included in the term "yom," the gradual action of rain over the years would leach the salt out of the soil and prepare the earth for the vegetation it was designed to sustain. Again, the inquirer may ask, "Could vegetation have multiplied in the brief span of a solar day, to the perfection of the botanical world?"

On the other side of the question is the evidence that the land appeared, according to the text itself, not as a saline ooze, but as "dry land." There is very exact significance in that first command of God, "Let the *dry land* appear." We are here dealing again with the suggestion of instancy, which is further advanced by the words, "and it was so." A time extension is neither expressed nor implied, and it is false to the sense of the text to insert such in the reading. Again, we must remember that we are dealing with that power which man can neither comprehend, emulate, nor limit, — the omnipotence of God. What He can do in an instant of time is beyond the grasp of the human mind, so we dare not limit His works, nor demand for them sweeping ages, when seconds would suffice. We also note that the botanical creations were

not in their present profusion of varieties, mutants and multiplied individuals, but only the parent plant of the original
species is intended. The years that followed cared for, by
natural production, all the present mass we witness today.

The exponents of the age-theory seem to forget the weakness of their argument in that this day, or yom, was half
dark and half light. Did these first created plants live two
hundred and fifty thousand years in absolute darkness? That
would be a miracle indeed. Also we note that the direct rays
of the sun did not reach the earth until the fourth day: did
these plants survive a sunless age of a quarter of a million
years or so? It would be highly probable that they could
survive a mere twenty-four hours in a sunless condition, but
scarcely for a great geological era. Not being able to make
a dogmatic decision as to the length of that day, we still take
the position that it was most probably a solar day, and pass
on to a consideration of the events of that day, just as they
are infallibly revealed in the writing of Moses.

The first event of this day is the formation of the oceans.
Please note that the text puts the seas in the plural, as that
is a matter of scientific interest. How Moses knew that there
were several oceans is a mystery, as neither he nor any other
man of his day had seen most of them! The peculiar nature
of this revelation is further seen when we note that Moses
says also that all these oceans have only one bed! This is of
course a well known and accepted fact in our day, but how
could he have known this? The text clearly states that God
said, "Let the waters under the heaven be gathered together
unto one place, and it was so." Indeed, it is so, as you can
clearly see by consulting the globe. You can see the Atlantic
and Pacific oceans come together down below South America;
that the Antarctic touches the Pacific; that the Arctic amalga-
mates with the Atlantic and the Pacific; at the position of
Gibraltar, the Mediterranean mingles with the Atlantic, and
even the Baltic meets the Atlantic at Skagerrak.

It could never be said of the land that it was gathered together into one place. It is broken and widely separated into many distinct pieces and places. Indeed, it is only at latitude sixty degrees south that the globe can be circumnavigated without bumping into land somewhere. But it is true of the oceans, that they occupy one vast and gigantic bed. They are in "one place" as far as the earth's structure is concerned.

How did Moses know this? In his day it was believed that the earth was flat, and that there was the one small ocean. Indeed, if a man had said in Moses' day that there was another and vastly larger ocean on the opposite side of the earth from them, he would have been locked up, or treated with the cruelty visited upon the mentally deficient in that rude and barbaric day. The ideas of the one small ocean with which they were acquainted were crude and weird in that day, and for thousands of years it was still believed that it was possible to sail off the end of the earth. It is impossible, then, that Moses could have spoken from purely human wisdom, and have said what he did here state, that all the oceans had only one great extensive bed.

At the same time he was careful to state that the seas are not all one body of water. He puts them in the plural. Again he was scientifically accurate, for while the oceans do have one bed they are nevertheless distinctly individual. There is a chemical difference between the waters of one ocean and any of the others. A fish taken out of the Atlantic, transported instantly across the continent of North America, and put in the Pacific Ocean, would not survive. When the fish pass from one kind of water to another, they take their time and acclimate themselves to the chemical differences by degrees.

The element of design is clearly shown again by the ratio of the land to the water of the sea. When the ocean gave up part of its domain to form the dry land, it surrendered with reluctance about one-fourth of its entire area. So that the oceans now occupy three-fourths of the globe, and the land area is one-fourth. To put the matter concretely, the entire globe has a surface of approximately one hundred and ninety-seven million square miles. The area of the oceans totals one hundred and forty-five million square miles, so that leaves a land surface of fifty-two million square miles. As a point of comparison we might note that the United States comprises only a little over three and three-quarter million square miles, so fifty-two million square miles is a respectable portion of the globe!

Now for the evidence of design in this exact ratio. We know that the amount of rainfall is governed by the ratio of ocean to land, and that on the square of the factor of increase or decrease. So that if the ocean had only one-half of its present preponderance, the earth would receive only one-fourth its present rainfall. This, in view of the increased area of the land, would make of the entire earth a Sahara desert in which vegetation would be almost, if not quite, impossible. On the other hand, if the area of the ocean should be increased to the extent of half the present land surface, the rest of the land would not be "dry land" at all, as the rainfall would be increased to four times its present average, making of the earth a vast swamp, in which man could not possibly support himself and his works So in preparing the earth for man, the Creator established, by design, the proportion of the land to the sea, as we have it today. There have, of course, been slight submergences, and minor emergences, but their total amount has been so negligible as to have no appreciable effect upon the ratio of the land to the sea.

It is no wonder then that God looked at the first work of that day, the sea, and called it good. It is so recognized today by all.

The ocean is "good" because of its beauty. There is nothing on the face of the globe that offers to beauty-loving mankind a more varying countenance than the sea. It is a thing of rare beauty when it sleeps in the quiet of a calm, with the brilliant blue of a tropic sky reflected in a solid sheet upon its unruffled surface. In the emerald green of the southern islands, in the cobalt blue of the middle tropics, or the steel gray of the northern waters, the ocean in calm is a thing of beauty.

Its beauty is only intensified in the thunder of a raging storm. When the waters pile up into grim, gray mountains, frosted on top like snowclad peaks by the flying spume, it is not only beautiful, but majestic. A spectacle of power that never lacks the very essence of grace, a clashing exhibition of force that thrills the soul of the onlooker by its very splendor, is the ocean in the grip of a heaving tempest.

Nowhere on the great planet, which we temporarily inhabit, is the vault of the sky so beautiful as it is over the sea. When the winds begin to shepherd their fleecy flocks of clouds off to the pasture lands, and the racing scud beneath seems to be reflected in the open sky, it is an object that entrances the very soul of the traveler. When the rising sun tints the sky above the sea, the artistic soul becomes drunk on color; and when at the close of day the sun sinks to rest in the broad expanse of the open water, to set the sky on fire with its dying blaze, all the poets in the world cannot do more than begin to express the indescribable beauty of the color riot that sets the heart leaping in the bosom of the beholder.

The supreme beauty of the sea is undoubtedly upon its marvelous floor. Down in the eternal moonlight on the floor of the sea, the transient visitor from the upper world is in a fairy-land that beggars description. Of all the accomplishments that man has been able to perfect, none is so amazing as his equipment for submarine observation and excursions. A trifle of its beauty may be filched from the floor of the sea by the aid of the glass-bottomed boats in the marine resorts, but the true wonders of that mysterious world can be appreciated only by one who is actually walking on the bottom.

Shut off from any sound except the soft hiss of the air-valve
in the helmet, to walk in a silent universe where motion is
retarded, and the law of gravity is *reversed*, so that a man
falls *up* instead of down, at every turn wonders that can never
be forgotten, greet the eye. Pastel shades of color unknown to
the rainbow of the upper realm, move in living splendor all
about. Weird and fantastic blossoms resolve themselves into
living creatures at the approach of man. Flowers such as no
earthly garden ever beheld bloom in ghostly splendor; the
ultimate experience of a living man is a pilgrimage to the
floor of a warm tropic sea. Whether on its surface, sailing
serenely in the sky that canopies its expanse, or walking
upon its floor, the ocean is a thing of beauty. In this it is
"good."

The ocean is "good" because of its saline content. What
would the life of man be without salt? Since salt is an appreciable ingredient in the blood-stream of man and the mammals alike, where would the life of the planet that demands
salt find an answer to this need, if the ocean had not been
created with its saline content?

Geology seeks to tell us that the ocean obtained its salt
content from great beds or deposits of salt in the land. The
waters, leaching out this substance over countless ages, deposited the salt in the sea as all the rivers reached it through
some means or another. This theory has several weaknesses,
the chief one being that the same textbook tells us that the
great beds of salt on and in the land were deposited there by
primeval seas! Since we have elsewhere written about the
mysterious nature of salt, we need not in this chapter comment on the problem of its origin by natural means, but will
simply state what must be an apparent fact, — the ocean contains salt because it was created that way!

The saline content of the ocean water varies according to
the section of the globe, but there is a simple reason for that.
The smallest quantity of salt found anywhere in the ocean

is one and three-fourths per cent; the highest is twelve per cent. The phenomena of evaporation and precipitation account for this most satisfactorily. We noted that as the clouds were formed by the ascending vapors the solids, including the salt, were left behind. Thus in tropical seas, where the evaporation is tremendously accelerated, the content of solids in the water would be much higher than at the poles, where evaporation is negligible. This introduces another problem in oceanography. In a few thousand years the oceans at the tropics, due to this high rate of evaporation, would soon become "dead seas" literally, so saline and laden with chemical solids as to make life impossible there, if it were not for the action of the mighty ocean currents that sweep up and down, back and forth, keeping the waters stirred, mixed, and mingled. The mechanism of this distribution is simple in the extreme: the saltier the water, the heavier it is, so the chemical laden water at the tropics sinks toward the bottom. This attracts the lighter water from the poles, and currents are formed much the same as winds are generated in the upper atmosphere, by the heavier, or colder, air, rushing in to the point where the resistance is the lowest.

The saline content of the ocean is essential to preserve the life of the sea. Soon the great bodies of water would be vast areas of corruption and the earth would be swept clean of life from the resulting epidemic, if the salt content should be removed suddenly.

The ocean is "good," again, because of the beneficial effect of its mighty rivers, called streams. These vast currents are absolutely beyond the power of man to produce or to control, yet they are essential to his existence in many parts of the globe. Consider the great Gulf Stream as an instance of this beneficence derived from a source beyond and above human control. This famous stream has been seen by innumerable visitors and residents in the state of Florida, where the stream leaves the Gulf of Mexico and parallels the Florida coast as it travels north. Most fishermen who have cast a line in the delightful waters of the Florida region have witnessed the odd line of cleavage between the main waters of the ocean and the current of the Gulf Stream. As clearly defined as the bank of a river on the land, the aqueous shores of the ocean define its beginning. There your boat may float at rest, one half in the waters of the ocean proper, and the other end in the totally different colored water of the stream. Along its edges the fishing is indeed wonderful.

This great stream leaves the Gulf of Mexico, from whence it takes its name, and parallels the coast of North America from the lower end of Florida to the region of Nova Scotia. As it leaves the Gulf with a temperature of eighty-six degrees Fahrenheit, and practically retains its warmth all the way, it has a tremendous influence on the climate of the lands it passes. The heat of the stream is still eighty-four degrees at the Georgia-Carolina border, and the warm temperate climate of these states is directly derived from this stream. Something of its tempering power on the surrounding atmosphere may be understood when we note that the stream is a thousand times the size of the mighty Mississippi River at that river's mouth; being seventy miles wide and something over three thousand feet deep.

An amusing attempt to explain the equable climate of Georgia was made by an old Colonial writer before the effect of the Gulf Stream was known. On a map, and in the accompanying reference, now in the possession of Judge Kuntz, at Atlanta, this old scientist said: "The Colony of Georgia owed its warm winters to the presence of great inland seas, called the Great Lakes, the largest of which, Lake Michigan, touched the State of Georgia on the northern boundary." Tell some of your Chicago friends that! This olden geographer says in just these words: "The mild breezes blowing across these vast inland seas keep the winters warm in the entire colony of Georgia." Tell that to your Chicago friends as well! That the winds that blow across Lake Michigan in the winter keep *Chicago* warm and temperate will be a new idea to them! Catch Moses making a mistake like that!

The coast of North America and Northern Europe would be a frozen waste without this stream. It alone makes the New England states habitable and makes life possible in Northern Europe as well. The British Isles would be frozen and abandoned without the stream, and even now, when the current swings a little wide of its general course, a near ice-age descends upon the old country, and suffering is tremendous. The Maritime Provinces of Canada owe their life and prosperity to this stream, and Nova Scotia would never have had her amazing and dramatic influence upon current human history without its near presence. It is near Nova Scotia that the current divides, one fork flowing past the Azores, to make those Atlantic isles habitable, and the other passing the British group, and repeating its beneficence there.

The reason for this division is tremendously interesting, and highly significant as well. The Gulf Stream is not the only one that we must reckon with. Out of Baffin Bay there swings the mighty Polar Stream, that is a worthy rival of the superior Gulf Stream. Up near Nova Scotia these mighty rivals meet, one rushing madly on to the north, the other as blindly seeking an escape to the south. Talk about "an irresistible force meeting an immovable object!" We almost have it here. In the silence of desperation, a titanic battle is waged between these two great streams, in which conflict the Polar Stream is the vanquished. Not able to overcome the superior power of the Gulf Stream, it is forced to dive deep to escape, and continue its journey south under the surface. So deep does it dive that it remains down until it reaches the vicinity of the West Indies, where it comes to the surface again, and with its Arctic breath cools the atmosphere there, and makes life possible in that tropical heat.

The result of this battle of the oceanic monsters is even more notable than this, as the Gulf Stream conquers its only rival at the cost of deflection from its course. The effect of the meeting is to bend the north-bound stream out of its path, and send it across to fulfill its ordained task, and warm the British Isles and the continent of Europe. So the tropic islands find relief from the oppressive heat, and the northern lands are released from the bondage of eternal winter, all through the goodness of the mighty sea. The why, and the how, of these great currents may long remain a mystery to us, but at least, when we note their beneficence to man, we cannot but admit that they shout aloud their testimony to the fact of design!

The ocean is called "good" because it is balanced to the needs of the earth. Note, for instance, that if the ocean's surface were one mile lower, all the continents would be joined by great ridges of dry land, and one would not be separated from the other. This would still leave the ocean with an average depth of a mile and a half, as certain sections of the sea are some six miles deep at the present time.

If, on the contrary, there were no mountains or plateaus, the ocean would cover the entire globe under nine thousand feet of water. There would then be no life on the planet but fish and such things as dwell in the ocean by nature, and the marvels of botany, biology, and anthropology would be undreamed of. This balance of the sea and land that we now observe is one of the reasons we agree with the Creator, who looked down and saw that it was "good." The contrary, of course, would be the case if the ocean ever burst its bounds, got out of control, and flooded the land.

What holds it in its place? Men in antiquity often speculated on this question, and many and varied were the ingenious answers that human reason advanced to account for this fact. There is, for instance, the ancient Persian map, that makes the earth flat, a bit longer than it is wide, and shaped much like a Persian war-shield. All about the edge of this map of the earth, the ancient scientist who drew it has depicted a row of mountains which he calls "The Mountains of Caif." With engaging ingeniousness he explains, "No eye hath as yet seen these 'Mountains of Caif.' But reason tells us they must be there, as otherwise the ocean would flow off the edge of the earth, and the sea would soon be dry"!

This, of course, is the best that human reason could do in that rude and unlearned age. But many centuries before that, the prophet and patriarch Job had written on the same subject, and said of God,

"He shut up the sea with doors,
When it brake forth as though it had issued forth
    from the womb;
He marked out for it His bound,
    And set doors and bars;
And said, Hitherto shalt thou come, but no farther!
And here shall thy proud waters be stayed!"

And the sea obeys that sublime command to this very hour. No matter how its fierce billows may hammer and roar, they are chained in the bands of limitation that Job so poetically expresses, testifying to the obedience of Nature to her Creator's commands.

The ocean is "good" because it feeds the world of mankind with a multitude of different foods. There is no need to enumerate the numbers of species and varieties that make up the vast and heterogeneous company we call fish; the ocean teems with them and man somewhere uses almost all for the purposes of food. The clams and oysters, and the vast world of the crustacea that dwell upon the ocean's floor, are all used by man somewhere and sometime for the purpose of sustaining his life. Even the gigantic Cetacea, those marvelous mammals which were created to dwell in the sea, are eaten by man. These whales are so vast, that one of them will supply forty tons of edible flesh, and the thrifty Japanese people can testify to its life-sustaining power.

In the ocean as well, there are many edible plants which enter into the daily diet of many peoples and races who dwell upon or near its shores. Some of these grow close to the border of the beach and are daily reaped by the land dwellers, while others are harvested by special equipment that sets out to brave the dangers of the deep and bring home the sustenance the ocean contains. It is indeed no exaggeration to say that out of the seas we get thousands of varieties of food, and the race of man in many lands can rise up and call the ocean blessed because it brings them their daily bread. The necessary meat-ration of many races comes entirely from the sea. It is the commissary and the cupboard of families and tribes all around the globe.

What would the Esquimaux do for food, in the frozen and barren north, if they did not harvest the sea? Fish or seal, polar bear or porpoise, sea-lion or giant whale, they eat the life that is indigenous to the salty deep. Fishing fleets set out from the safety of the shore to spread their sails like the wings of gulls on the breast of the heaving main, to garner the crop that is life and fortune to them. The sea is "good:" it feeds the land.

The ocean is "good" because of its healing powers. The very breeze that blows across its surface absorbs the elements of healing that are native to the billowy brine, and passes them on to the land dweller. One of the commonest healing agents the ocean contains is the element called iodine. This is perhaps one of the most universal drugs known to man. It is found in almost every home medicine chest, and in the first-aid kits of all expeditions, hunting and fishing parties, and mountain-scaling groups. This medicine is found in the ocean, and one of the commonest methods of procuring it is by burning a sea weed, called kelp, and extracting the iodine from the ashes.

It is and should be the first thought in wounds, cuts, and general abrasions, as it has the power to prevent, as well as to cure, infection. The first red signal of a wound that has begun to fester is an incentive to the average man to reach for the iodine bottle. And no man can say how many amputations have been avoided since iodine was discovered.

Iodine in the pre-natal development of the individual is absolutely essential for a normal babe; the absence of it means that dread type of idiocy known as cretinism. In the mature adult an absence of iodine in the thyroid gland means that the individual thus deficient is almost certain to develop goiter, and one of the first things given the sufferer from this disease is a course of iodine, in either the potassium or sodium form.

Men who conduct expeditions in far-away lands do not need to boil their drinking water any more, as we have learned that ten drops of iodine (the ordinary ten per cent solution regularly purchased at the drug store) in a gallon of water will make that water absolutely safe in forty minutes. So into the suspected drinking water we put a few drops of iodine and set the container aside, confident that every pathogenic bacterium will be dead and harmless within the hour.

Practically the entire earth's supply of iodine is in the sea. It is extremely soluble, and has all been leached out of the land ages ago, and the ocean holds our only supply. No wonder God called it good! Out of its waters, from its creatures, and its plants we get no less than two hundred different healing agencies. They were all there when we came to understand our need of them, and knowing their power and value the Creator called the sea that contained them, "good."

The ocean is "good" because it is a vast treasure chamber of untold values. The ancient Croesus was a pauper compared to the man who will some day learn to garner the treasures of the sea. Some of them we have learned to glean for our coffers, but it is a pitifully small percentage of the unbounded wealth that remains there, awaiting the genius who can pick it up.

Here and there we find a pearl, and shout with gladness over the few thousands of dollars our find nets us. And yet there are over a billion tons of gold in the protozoic ooze of the floor of the sea, and many times that amount in suspension in its waters! Radium, that sells for a king's ransom for a gram, is present in such quantities in the ocean that if we could gather it all, we could sell it at a profit for ten dollars a ton! If we could even learn to harness the waves of the sea and use its mighty power as we harness our waterfalls on the land, we could write our own figures for the fortune that would accrue. We boast of our ability to tie up the forces of nature in our human projects, and yet the power of a thousand Niagaras pounds daily on the shores of the Californian coast alone, utterly wasted so far as human use is concerned.

Well then, because it is a thing of beauty, of benefit, and of value, we agree with Moses that the ocean is "good." Yet how could Moses, who never saw the seas, know all this? Not by human wisdom, we are sure.

The ocean teems with evidence of specific creation, and refutations of the theory of organic evolution. Its myriad creatures shout with clarion voices the fact of design, and the "fortuitous concurrences of accidental circumstances" finds no place in its life-story.

One case in point is the sea horse, called scientifically Hippocampus. This tiny creature is one of the weird mysteries of ocean biology, and presents many fascinating problems for the investigator. In the first place, to be strictly correct it must be classed as a marsupial. This is the order of life that has the abdominal pouch for the carrying of the young, as in the case with the Australian kangaroo, or the American opossum. But while Hippocampus has this abdominal pouch in which the young mature, the sea horse is a fish in the true sense of the word! In the second place, we note that the abdominal pouch on Hippocampus is possessed by the male, and *not* by the female! This startling anomaly cannot be explained by the theory of evolution. The female sea horse lays her eggs in the pouch of the male, and he brings forth the young. At what stage in evolution, when, where, and by what variants was the marsupial pouch transferred from the female to the male? These questions are unanswerable; Hippocampus is a living evidence of the fact of special creation; most certainly *he was made that way*.

In a chapter so brief as this we cannot of course exhaust the subject, but will have to be content with this simple setting forth of facts that show beyond the shadow of doubt that Moses indeed was in perfect accord with modern science when he said God placed His seal on the finished work of the creation of the sea, and called it "good." It is, indeed, "good."

From the very moment of its discovery by man, the sea has been recognized as a mighty evidence of the creative power of God, and as a testimony that thinking men have ever acknowledged. Even to this present hour, there is a convincing voice that the sea possesses, and few indeed are the sons of men so brutish and degraded that they are insensible to this great message of God's divine power. We have known many men whose lives have been cast with the sea as the background of their daily toil, but we have never met a seafaring man who was an atheist!

Even the thoughtless and unthinking, the careless and the unheeding, turn alike with the natural philosopher to thoughts of God's grandeur when the sea is in turmoil. Whether it be the dweller on the land, who goes to the cliff's edge to see the storm-tossed waves lashing in baffled fury against the unyielding shore; or whether it be the sailor who fights for his life when his vessel is gripped in the fearsome power of the storm, the humblest are moved to awe at the might of this creature that only the Almighty can control!

Indeed, one of the most exquisite bits of unconscious humor in all The Book, is David's observation on the conduct of his fellowmen in the time of storm. In the Psalm that is numbered one hundred and seven, the writer says:

"They that go down to the sea in ships,
    That do business in great waters;
These see the works of the Lord,
    And His wonders in the deep.
For He commandeth, and raiseth the stormy wind,
    Which lifteth up the waves thereof.
They mount up to the heavens,
They go down again to the depths;
    Their soul is melted because of trouble.
They reel to and fro,
    They stagger like a drunken man,
And are at their wits' end.
Then they cry unto the Lord in their trouble,
And He bringeth them out of their distresses!"

So even the man who never thinks of God, and his relation to this Heavenly Being, turns to Him, when the storm rages and the waves toss his ship high. The classic illustration, of course, is the famous case of the atheist whose ship was wrecked on a voyage to Europe, and as the boats were lowered away, made the night vocal with his cries of "Oh, God, help us!"

Yet the voice of the sea is as much a praise of God as is the thunder of its storm.

For generations the poet has been asking, "What are the wild waves saying?" The answer seems to be obvious; they are chanting the Doxology! In all the realm of nature, there is no greater testimony to creation than the voice of the sea.

This is seen not only in the world and experience of men, it is written many times in The Book as well. The sea is mentioned in the Bible five hundred and five different times, and scores of these references speak of God as its Creator. So in the ninety-fifth Psalm, the inspired writer says, "The sea is His, and He made it; and His hands formed the dry land." Truly, the realm of nature heeds the injunction of the Psalmist, when he says, "Let the heaven and earth praise Him, the seas, and everything that moveth therein."

A striking instance of this is found in the amazing work of the greatest man of science America has so far produced. We refer to the late Matthew Fontaine Maury, who has been called "The Pathfinder of the Seas." He is the father of the science of oceanography, the dean of all physical geographers, and perhaps the founder of the school of meteorology as well. His genius was responsible for the Annapolis Academy, where our naval officers are trained, and every civilized nation on earth honored him lavishly in the days of his life, save only his own country, that he served so well. Our recognition of his greatness was posthumous, but he is at last enshrined in one of the highest niches in our hall of fame.

In Richmond, Virginia, there stands a statue commemorating this man, that is one of the most beautiful and suggestive bits of sculpture in our nation. The venerable scientist sits with the charts of the sea that he helped to conquer in one hand, and the Bible, the source of inspiration, in the other. Back of him is the globe, the world that he knew so well, with the fish and the birds telling of his conquests of the air and the seas.

In his day, there were no charts and sailing lanes, but the master of each vessel sailed as his fancy dictated. One day, during a temporary illness, the great scientist was lying in his bed, while his eldest son read to him from the Bible. While reading in the eighth Psalm that tells of nature's contribution to man, he read this verse: "The fowls of the air, and the fish of the sea, and whatsoever passeth though the paths of the sea." The listener interrupted the reading to say, "Read that again." When his son had complied, the scientist said, "It is enough. If the Word of God says there are paths in the sea, they must be there, and I am going to find them!" Within a few years he had done that very thing, and the liners that sail the seas today, all follow the paths that he marked out for them. We can think of no more fascinating pleasure that could come to our readers, than the perusal of the life of this great man. (The best biography and record of his work is entitled "Matthew Fontaine Maury" by Charles L. Lewis, and may be procured from The Maury Association, Richmond, Virginia.) This instance is given here simply to show that even the sea in all its majesty and splendor, must conform to what is written in the Word of God!

From this vast realm of the sea, the sources and origin of the blessing called salt, the Lord Jesus draws His most flattering designation of the nature of the Christian. No higher dignity can be conferred upon the believer than that which Jesus conferred when He said, "Ye are the *salt* of the earth!" Not only do we say that salt is the "spice of life" but we also remember that it is healing, preserving, cleansing; and above all else, it is conducive to thirst. This is indeed the chief characteristic of salt; it makes folks thirsty! So our Lord draws this great illustration from the sea, the source of salt, and says, "Ye are the salt of the earth." In other words, by the very fact of your presence in your circle of life, you should make men and women thirst for the Water of Life that is Christ Jesus. Do you?

And finally, the glory of the reign of the returning Christ is described by the prophet Isaiah with a figure that comes from the sea. Speaking of that time when the Son of God shall reign on this earth for the Kingdom age, the prophet says, ". . . for the earth shall be full of the knowledge of the Lord, as the waters cover the sea!" From the hour of creation, then, to the end of the reign of the Lord Jesus, the voice of the sea speaks to men of the greatness and the might of God. What need of human witnesses when the creations of God are unanimous in

praise of Him! Let us humbly bow before Him who hath created the sea, and, with the diapason that comes from this
mighty organ of praise, blend our voices in the song of recognition that too long we have withheld from Him Whose power
formed the sea.

Geology and the Rock of Ages

CHAPTER FIVE

Geology and the Rock of Ages

"AND God said, Let the dry land appear, and it was so." With such simple words as these Moses introduces and concludes his observation on the amazing mystery of the appearance of that section of the globe upon which we have our habitation. The dry land appeared. That is the simplest statement we ever read, of the most profound event, and any child can comprehend it. The dry land *appeared*. The wisest man in the world cannot add to the conclusive information there conveyed. This is one of the many questions that for so long have vexed the inquiring mind of the average man. The dry land is an absolute essential to the life of this globe; but where did it come from?

Aside from the answer of Moses, the only theory advanced to date is the "primal continent" idea. Ages before this present land appeared, we are told, there were other continents and islands where the ocean now is. These were gradually worn down by erosion, and the present layers of matter slowly grew upon the floor of the sea. Age fled by upon the heels of age, until suddenly the bosom of the whole round globe heaved in a mighty convulsion, and the ancient continents sank. Then the present land emerged in the giant upheaval, and we now occupy the sections of the planet that were once under the sea.

Let us glance at this theory for a moment, and see how much that helps the problem of origins. It seems most unsatisfactory to the earnest student. When the student inquires, "Where did the dry land come from, and what is its origin?" it seems most unsatisfactory to reply, "It came from other dry land, that was previously in existence." Even if we grant that this present section of the earth that is fitted for habitation was formed under the sea, out of what was it formed? If it came from other land already in existence, where did pre-existing land come from? The issue is further confused when we note that the floor of the sea is also laid down in "layers," called strata, and is identical in this regard with the structure of the mountain range. In boring some of the oil wells in the ocean on the Pacific Coast, we have had the opportunity to compare the log of the well with the logs of others drilled in the mountains of the back country, and there seem to be as many "layers," and the same layers, in the ocean as in the land!

Also, it does not help the problem to find that in many of these strata, supposedly laid down under water, we find the perfectly articulated skeletons of land-dwelling mammals. These osseous evidences would have been scattered widely by the action of the waters long before they could have been covered to a safe depth by the slow process of natural erosion; and catastrophe is the only present answer to this apparent complication.

We remember at this point that Moses states such a catastrophe. "But the earth *had become* empty and unfurnished . . ." He continues by informing us that prior to the work of the First Day (and, indeed, up to the second work of the Third Day), the entire globe was covered with water. So that the evidences of submergence that we see in the present dry land may be dated back to the catastrophe there mentioned by Moses, and are not necessarily proof that the "Primal Continent" idea is established. Back of the primal continents there will always be the vast silence that greets the query, "And where did *they* in turn come from?" There *is* no other explanation than that of Moses: "And God said . . . and it was so."

The dry land, upon examination, shows itself to be made of various materials. Rocks of all varieties are common to all parts of the earth, as is also soil. It is this latter that is the mystery, and that testifies so eloquently to creative design in its structure and origin. It must not be supposed that intelligence will be satisfied with the puerile explanation of materialism, that the soil is simply rocks eroded to a more or less powdery form. There are in the soil several ingredients, notably, decayed animal and vegetable matter, various calcareous substances, pulverized rocks, and last but most important, enzymes. It is the presence of these latter that so thoroughly disposes of the theories of the mechanical school of naturalism.

We all know that there are certain natural chemical reactions that normally proceed at a very slow rate, which can be greatly increased by the action of an agent. When a foreign substance is added to a mixture or combination to hasten chemical changes, this added agent is called a "catalyst." Catalysts are very familiar to the student of chemistry, as they are inorganic and are constantly used in the laboratory. These enzymes we are discussing may be likened in the organic world to the catalysts of the inorganic kingdom. The enzymes, however, are of biologic origin, and are inherent in the structure of the cells. They are found in all living cells of all creatures, plant, animal or human, and it is they that enable the cells to carry on the various processes that are chemically essential to the continuance of the life of the cells.

Thus the farmer scatters certain chemical fertilizers on the soil in which he has planted certain crops. These elements may be nitrates, ammonia, albuminoid ammonia, or any other elements essential to the life of the plant he desires to grow. *It is entirely by the action of these enzymes that the plant is able to take these elements and turn them into new structures,* and thus provide food for man and beast. If it were not for the action of these enzymes the fertilizer would remain just that; but the enzymes so change the nature of the elements thus added that they are organized into breakfast, dinner or supper, instead of remaining forever chemical fertilizer in free form!

While most enzymes act within the structure of the cells that contain and create them, some of them are sent out as conquering armies to carry on conquest in foreign territory! Thus the enzyme named "ptyalin" is sent out by the salivary glands to act externally and to break down the particles in the masticated food, while the food is still in the mouth. These busy little bodies are never exhausted or fatigued, but have apparently unlimited power to perform their function of conversion of one substance into another, and they literally keep the world moving by their amazing abilities and powers. For they can reverse their process at will. An enzyme that will *break down* a certain substance will *synthetize* or build up that same structure under reversed conditions! That is to say, the same enzyme that arouses the destruction of a substance will assemble the elements of that substance and cause it to come into being. Their presence in the soil is therefore seen as essential if the world of botany is to continue to exist.

These busy little workmen are particular about their field of service, and most of them will act on only one structure or substance. A few will act upon all the elements of a very restricted group, provided that group is closely related. Intelligence has been given to these minute individuals to know infallibly the object for which they were created, and to concentrate during all their lifetime on that one substance. They never scatter their energies by essaying each others' tasks, but stay rigidly on the job for which they were each created.

Their power is amazing. They are active in the most minute amounts, or numbers, and are not subject to fatigue. It is stated that enzyme invertase can hydrolyze one million times its weight in cane sugar, without any appreciable loss of energy! The only way their power can be inhibited or frustrated is by the very nature of their own efforts. For when the enzyme has changed all the elements within reach, it is surrounded by the substance it is designed to produce, and has no more raw material upon which to work. But place near it

more matter to be hydrolyzed and it instantly springs into activity, as though it knew nothing of fatigue or diminished
power, as indeed it apparently does not.

Their chemical nature is at present unknown, as is their
origin. They are a mystery in every sense of the word, and
testify to the fact of creation by the very nature of their existence. The hydrolytic enzymes function in their task of transmutation of elements by reducing them first to a liquid state;
the autolytic group act without the aid of any agency whatever,
and the third group act by oxidation. All three varieties are
in the soil in teeming myriads; and it is their presence there
that is inexplicable. Where did they come from? Who put
them there? Who invented them, and gave them their amazing power? They unite in a single voice to cry aloud the fact
that Moses here records in this paragraph on the Third Day:
The soil is a creature of God, a thing that He created. Let us
examine this dry land of which Moses writes, and see what
evidence it will afford of this fact of creation.

The first and simplest argument is from topography. The
very fact of the rugged shape of the dry portion of the planet
is an evidence of God's forethought and provision for the
creatures that were later to occupy the earth. It may truly be
said that mountains testify of creation, and of the truth of this
narrative by their very presence. Their testimony of creation
is seen in the fact of design as displayed in the manner in which
mountains make the earth habitable for man.

They make the flow of rivers possible, and they govern to a
large extent the differences in climate. All the earth's supply
of drinking water is governed by the mountains, even where
there are none! This seems anomalous, but a moment of reflection will convince the reader that this is so. If the face of
the earth were level and low, the earth would be a vast swamp;
if it were level and high the earth would be a gigantic desert.
"All the rivers run into the sea . . ." because of the slope from
the mountain peak down to the water level of the ocean, no

matter how far away that may be. In these high levels, called mountains, the water is stored, to run as springs, brooks, creeks, and finally rivers, down to the thirsty plains below. In the lowlands, where the mountains are no longer visible, their beneficence is still dispensed. This storage of water controls, to a large degree, the source of supply that is tapped by wells. If the conditions are right, as in the case of mountains on two sides of the lowland, artesian wells may eventuate so far from them as to puzzle the casual beholder. In the weary days when there is no rain, the mountains provide water and keep us alive.

They aid in the establishment of the climate, by breaking up certain wind currents and influencing others. If the Andes mountains were on the opposite side of the continent, all South America would be a vast desert wilderness where man could not exist except under most trying circumstances. Mountains are ubiquitous, occurring in the islands of the sea, and in all the continents on the face of the earth. At both poles, and at the equator alike, the mountains tower up to the sky, silently performing their function of making the earth a fit place for man's existence. What an amazing evidence they offer of the grace and provision of the Creator!

They also testify to the truth of the Mosaic account of their origin by the fact that they were not originated where they are. At some time past they *were* elevated to form the present topography so beneficial to man, exactly as Moses states. They speak to every intelligent heart this account of mighty stress and strain in the twisted structure evidenced where erosion has bared their flanks and made plain their formation. Mighty canyons with their serrated indentations and protrusions show that if they could be pressed together, the protuberances of one side wall would fit exactly into the indentations on the opposite side, thus conclusively testifying that once they were one, and have been rent asunder by some stupendous power. This was catastrophic, cataclysmic, and any school of geology that fails to take account of this fact is doomed to oblivion sooner or later, and will ultimately find its way into the junk heap of a scientific limbo, where so many false theories of the past now peacefully repose in perpetual slumber.

The presence of the amazing numbers of fossils in the present mountains testifies to the accuracy of Moses; they *were* once all under water. One of the major difficulties that challenges our reasoning processes is the fact that many of these fossils are the same types of life that are alive today. But since these living forms with which we are familiar were all created after the Third Day of this creative week, it puzzles us to understand how they could have been in existence when the mountains were submerged under the aqueous blanket. It may be, of course, that all of our present fossils have been formed since this week of creation. We know that there have been many geological catastrophies in these historic times. It has been our personal privilege to see startling geological changes made by volcanic action and also by earthquake. Sometimes flood joins its devastating forces to other material upheavals working striking changes upon a once familiar terrain.

In the case of the Pacific coast mountains, which are called the youngest in geology, it may be that they have been forced up since Moses penned these words. There is no adequate system of chronology affiliated with the science of geology when it comes to dating rock systems. The man who dabbles in that field confesses himself to be an absurd guessiologist. However and whenever these fossils were formed, at least they all testify to this indubitable fact — at one time the present mountain systems were submerged, even as Moses has said. These mountains most certainly were once under water, — and the story of their emergence is most correctly told in these words, "And God said, Let the waters be gathered together into one bed, and *let the dry land appear.*"

The mountains are the storehouse of treasure with which

God has stocked them. Mineral deposits are found, it may be six or seven miles down the side of a mountain, in such accessible places that man has only to run his tunnel in, in order to strike these bodies of wealth and harvest them. What a task it would be if the land were all level and this level were thrust up as a plateau above the crest of the waters, and man in his quest for metal and treasure had to dig down the five or six miles of the mountain's height, plus the length of his tunnel, before he could reach these stores. He would still be in a stone age, or at best be using just such small amounts of mineral and metal as might chance to be on, or near, the surface. All these things, coupled with the fact of their varying beauty, and indescribable influence on the poetry, art, and science of man, combine to testify that Moses was right when he said: "And God saw that it was good."

We have often noted the prominent place the mountains occupy in the pages of the Bible. Having always lived in their region, never for more than a few months, at most, out of their influence, we have been interested to see how God's Word mentions them so often, and in so many ways. So many of His amazing dealings with men have been conducted in connection with mountains that it seems to savor of design, rather than chance. The word itself occurs in the Old and New Testaments a few over six hundred times, and many individuals are named in the sacred record. There appear by name some two score mountains and hills, and there is a special work of God's beneficence to man in connection with each so named.

Thus we read of Ararat, where the ark grounded in the days of Noah. The ark, of course, is recognized as a portrayal of the grace that is in Jesus Christ; it being He alone Who can carry the trusting soul safely through the waters and the disasters of judgment. There is special significance, then, in the fact that it was in the mountains that the eight who were saved found their final resting place, and came forth to occupy a new world and to live a new life.

Mount Seir is also named as the place where Esau found refuge and rest. There he became the prince and the patriarch of a vast people, and kings reigned among those who were called Edomites, after the name they gave to their land, Edom. Long before there was any king in Israel, Edom had an established dynasty, and the red sandstone city they built on Mt. Seir has recently been uncovered by archeological research. The entire account has thus been vindicated, to the chagrin of the critic, whose sole aim is to destroy the Word of God by his criticism. In this case, however, the red city of Edom speaks for the Bible once again, and the Mountain of Seir stands as a living testimony to the truth of the sacred record.

Then there is Mount Moriah, the place of sacrifice and salvation. The two, of course, always go together. What moving memories cluster about that great event; where a man by faith assured his son that God would Himself provide a lamb! This is the first place in the story of redemption where one is willing to offer his only and beloved son for the sake of pleasing God; it seems to shadow the coming event where God, who there provided the lamb, ended sacrifice forever by the gift of His only begotten Son.

Mount Sinai will always be remembered as the place where Jehovah met Moses, and there gave to him the book of the law, and made Himself known to men. Time will not permit of more than the mention of Horeb, called the mountain of God; it was here Aaron died, and Moses brought forth the water from the rock. Then there is Pisgah, from which Moses viewed the promised land, and Carmel, where the idols were cast down and their worshippers perished. The Scripture also tells us of Tabor, on which the Saviour was transfigured, and where men heard the very voice of the Living God testify that Jesus was the Beloved Son. There is also Zion, given as the picture of the enduring might of the church of Jesus Christ, and Olivet, where the Lord Jesus was so deep in sorrow. From this last-named mountain He departed in the ascension, and back to its peak, says the prophet Zechariah, He will surely come again. Finally, it was on a small round hill called Calvary, that Jesus shed His blood that all who believed on Him might be saved. Most certainly mountains occupy a place of dignity and splendor in the Book. Like all the dry land He called into being, God says of them, "It was good."

The structure of the dry land may be likened with great truth to the pantry of a provident and wise parent, who looks ahead to the needs of coming days and makes provision far in advance. The shelves are the structures and the strata; their contents are the provisions supplied. When we were small children we lived for some time on a mountain ranch in the high Sierra Nevada mountains, and like most of the mountain ranches forty or more years ago, we were isolated part of the year by rigid winter weather. There was no corner grocery store upon which to rely, and the idea of a delicatessen store was as foreign to us as it is to the cliff dwellers, or to one who dwells in the midst of the Sahara desert. I doubt if the family owned even a can opener!

When the harvest days brought their surplus of every good thing, Mother spent busy days laying up a store for the lean days to come. Jars were filled, certain fruits and vegetables were dried; others were put in adequate containers, and rapidly the great pantry filled against the day of need. Mother's pantry was a wonderful place; I can shut my eyes and almost see it now. There were shelves, one above the other, laden with everything the mind of man could desire, and all waiting to be appropriated by appetites that never lacked in appreciation! There was a shelf of cereals, dried beans and peas, and certain flours of corn and wheat. Then there was a shelf of interesting things, such as jars of peaches, great Bartlett pears, and dried apricots and apples. Above this again there was a shelf far more admirable in the eyes of a small boy; it held the jams and jellies and the preserves! While the very highest shelf of all, held, among other things, the cookie jar; too high, alas, to be reached, even with the help of a broom. That was the one mistake Mother made; we always felt that the cookies and the jams should be on the bottom shelf, the only one we could reach! She had other ideas, however, and her authority being supreme, we had to wait until the providence that provided these things also dispensed them at the appropriate time.

This earth on which we live may be likened to this pantry. It is the storehouse of God, on Whose shelves He has placed every good and perfect thing that man may need. All these blessings are placed within the reach of man, as his need grows. So year by year we learn to unlock the storehouse where God has placed certain things for our generation, and later men will learn new secrets in the day they are needed: The earth will always be able to supply the needs of the dwellers who are intelligent enough to reap her harvests and her benefits. We need only to go to the pantry of God and take what we need from the sea, the air, and the dry land. Especially the dry land.

Some years ago in Pennsylvania there dwelt a man of large means who had one splendid son. As he did not desire to spoil the boy with the idea of too much wealth, he raised the lad to believe that he would always have to earn his own living. The father let the boy choose his own schools as he grew older, and he put him through college and university, and then gave him a post-graduate course in an institution of technology. When the boy had the finest education he could get, he announced to his father that he was ready to go to work as soon as he found out what he wished to do. The father asked the son to come to his office the next morning for a conference, and when the boy arrived his father greeted him with a certified check for fifty thousand dollars! When the lad expressed his amazement his father said: "Altho I am a man of immense means, that is all you can ever expect from me whether I live or die. I have arranged my affairs so that my entire estate will go to philanthropic institutions in which I am interested, and that is all you will ever receive from me. I have given you the best education that money can provide, I have tried to give you self-reliance and ambition, and fifty thousand dollars with which to begin. My son, if you can't succeed with that, you are not worth helping any more!" The boy agreed most heartily, and said, "That is much more than I ever expected to have, and Dad, I'll make good."

Day after day as they met at the breakfast table the father would ask the son if he had decided what he intended to do, and every day the lad said he was still hunting for the right opportunity to invest his money, training and life. Then he dropped out of sight for ten days, and when he returned he said, "Dad, I know what I am going to do. I've found just what I have been looking for, and I have bought the old Wilkinson place." His father cried, "What! The Wilkinson place?" "Yes, sir," the boy replied, "I've done just that." "That's what comes of giving a nutty boy money," groaned the father. "Why, son, don't you know that three generations of better farmers than you will ever be, starved to death on that farm?"

The lad replied, "Yes, I know that, Dad, but I don't intend to farm it. I do not believe that God ever spread out eight hundred acres on the face of this earth and expected a man to starve to death on top of it. I intend to go down and see what is underneath." "How much did you pay for it?" his father inquired. With a grin the boy said, "Two thousand eight hundred eight dollars and no cents." "No sense is right," the disgusted man retorted. "Son, you had better give me the rest of that fifty thousand dollars, to keep for you until you get some brains." But the boy good-naturedly refused, saying he needed it to explore his new project. Pessimistically his dad warned him he would be pouring money down a rat hole, that when he was broke there would be no more help for him, and prophesied all manner of evil, with sundry caustic comments on the schools that would graduate a fellow knowing so little.

Undaunted, the lad began his exploration, and at a reasonably shallow depth he struck a magnificent vein of coal. His father went about for a week with his hat over one eye and his thumb hooked into the armpit of his vest, crowing to every friend he could get to listen: "I told you that boy of mine is the smartest youngster this town ever saw! I told you he had brains and would put himself on the top of the heap!" To the boy he said, "Now, son, we'll organize a company and float a development, and sell this coal and you will be a rich man in a short time," But the boy said, "No, sir, *we* will do nothing of the kind. *We* are not in this, but I am going on down and see what is under the coal." His father pleaded in vain, the boy was obdurate; and although his father said, "You've been lucky once, better use some sense, and let well enough alone," he persisted, and a few weeks later discovered a splendid vein of ore under his coal.

The buttons on his father's vest almost snapped off with pride, and once more his friends had to hear him boast, "With a smart boy like that, and a father like me to encourage him, that boy will never stop. He'll just go on, and on, and own everything he wishes." To his son the father explained, "Now with this iron and coal so closely associated we can organize a company, start a smelter, and be so situated that none can compete with us in this territory. How much shall we organize for?" The lad modestly said, "*We* won't organize at all! I wish to know what is under the iron!" And in spite of the bitter cries of his Dad he put a mortgage on his entire estate to get more capital to operate, and succeeded in finding an extensive oil field on his holdings.

Until the day that he died, he was not able to spend the income that accrued to him from a bit of dry land where three generations almost starved to death, because they never opened up the pantry to see what the Father had put on the shelves for any child who had faith and confidence enough to look!

There are minerals almost innumerable in the dry land, and we have only to tap the earth and open its stores to garner what we need. Iron which we smelt into steel is one evidence of the treasure with which this globe is stocked. We bend it to our purpose to use it for navigation, to aid us in agriculture, to help in architecture, and the manufacture of all sorts of useful articles. It is even used on the instruments through whose aid we carry on research in various fields of science. Accessible, strong, malleable, susceptible to welding into pipes and carriers hundreds of miles long, if necessary or desired, it is man's chief servant today. Occurring in abundant quantities in numerous locations, by its ubiquity available to all men everywhere, it is the very foundation upon which our civilization rests. Verily, the "iron age" is the age of the conquest of the earth, and without its help man would still be the fugitive on the face of the earth he became soon after the Fall from Eden's estate! For defense, or for offense, iron is still supreme, and will so remain for a long time. The giant weapons of war that belch out their thunder against the foe are made of iron, and so is the armor that resists the fire of the opposing forces. The blade of the plow that turns the soil is made of this precious metal, as is the nail that pins the house together. The man of science who studies the nature of iron gazes at it through a microscope that is composed of the material he studies, and the physician who rides in a chariot made of iron administers this same metal to the patient he calls to see! Take iron out of the civilization of the twentieth century, and its very fabric would collapse. If its value is to be measured by the service it renders, iron is a precious metal indeed!

So is copper. This is supposed to be one of the "baser," or cheaper metals, but why have fortunes been made from copper? Because it occurs in huge quantities, and has made itself indispensable to man. Imagine the millions of miles of copper wires that carry the electricity of commerce across the face of this land alone! Contemplate the networks of copper wires that criss-cross the terrain for no other purpose than to carry the voice and the words of men! And even when the radio is perfected to the stage it has achieved today, copper, although to that extent replaced as a message-carrying factor, is still essential to the construction of the radio!

The electric energy that fires the gas in the engine of the automobile, tractor or airplane, is conveyed to the place of ignition by the channel supplied by copper wire. The great shells that menace the enemy who seeks to invade our fair land ride through the bore of the gun that shoots them on a base of copper, and the fuse that ignites them upon impact owes its origin to this metal as well.

When we remember that the rocks contain some two thousand different metals and minerals in various forms, we can see that the Father has in very truth stocked the pantry of the dry land with abundant provision for our every need. For to these things we must not forget to add such things as oils, salts, oxides, and precious gems; all of which are found on these "pantry" shelves. The fact of oil is in itself marvelous enough to deserve a special chapter in this series on creation. Black, filthy in appearance, contaminating all it touches, repulsive to the nostrils of civilized man, it yet serves him in many marvelous manners. The wheels of industry spin because of the gentle influence of certain refinements of this black mass. Night is robbed of its terror in many far-away places by the illumination that comes from further refinements of this unattractive substance. Automobiles speed across the land, fast launches cleave the bosom of the vast and briny deep, and graceful birds of man's devising float like the substance of dreams on the very air we breathe, all driven on by a substance that is derived from common petroleum. Oil! No wonder men call it "Black Gold," when it is so great an aid in the affairs of men, and when such fortunes have been made by its very presence in the soil some fortunate men happened to own.

So also with coal, given to man for power and heat. How the world would have progressed to its present stage of developed comfort and convenience for man without the aid of coal is difficult to imagine. It is a long span that has been builded by coal, from the day the first steamboat and the first steam railroad engine began to run for the benefit of the human race. What wonders have been brought to pass by this simple fact: a certain rock, called coal, will burn! Great industries have been erected upon this fact, cities have been lighted and continents conquered because of it, and even the ocean lost most of its terrors for the intrepid men who sailed its watery wastes, because of coal. The story is too well known to require retelling here; we merely remind the reader of the fact of coal as an evidence of God's forethought and provision for the needs of His creatures. Certainly none can deny that it was formed ages before it was required and it must have been brought into being in anticipation of a future need.

When we stop to consider the fact that the rocks of the earth also contain a type of stone called "precious," we see an argument for specific creation and design that is unanswerable. For almost everything in this world there may perhaps be a useful purpose; but certainly not for the gem stones. There is no creature that eats them, they do not break down into fertilizer as do most other natural structures; they never decompose to form soil as do the common rocks; their very hardness, in which partially lies the secret of their value, precludes such a possibility. No other creature in this world gets any use or value out of the precious stones; they above all other things were created by God for the pleasure and the enjoyment of His children.

That they are the result of a specific creation is evident from their structure. No matter what precious stone is under consideration, it is always built on a certain geometric plan and pattern which is somatic to all the individuals of that classification. Thus the diamond may be recognized as a diamond wherever it is found, and an emerald is the same the world over. Not only is this a fact in the case of the individual stone, but it remains a fact no matter how small a stone may be crushed. It is impossible to powder a precious stone into anything but smaller, but none the less perfect, stones, of that same precious variety.

As an instance, the amethyst is a crystal which occurs in the shape of a rhomboid. A great cluster of these stones lies before me as I write, and every one of the cluster is a perfect rhomboid. If one of these crystals is detached from the group and struck a sudden blow with a hammer, it will shatter into a hundred pieces, *each of which will be a perfect rhomboid.* We then gather up these particles and put them in an iron mortar and crush them with an iron pestle. When we have ground them as fine as sand, we examine this purple sand under a low-powered magnifier, and we see that each grain of the sand is a perfect rhomboid. We then put the grains of sand between the steel rollers of a powerful mill and grind them as fine as flour. Then we examine the specks of this purple flour under a microscope, and every tiny speck is a minute rhomboid, as perfect as the large one we started with. It is impossible so to crush an amethyst that it loses its structural pattern; all you can do is to make of an amethyst many smaller ones.

This same fact is noted in the case of all the other precious stones as well. No matter what their pattern may be, that pattern remains all through the crushing process, with the geometric perfection thereof unimpaired. The gem stone that is commonly called the topaz crystallizes on a geometrical pattern that is orthorhombic. This is commonly called a trimetric structure, possessing three unequal axes at right angles to each other. When we pulverize a topaz, it divides and subdivides upon this exact pattern. Just as the purple "flour" of a ground amethyst maintains a structure inherent in its division, so the yellow dust of the topaz always remains orthorhombic for each tiny fragment. The garnet, as another instance, always has a structure that is isometric. We have an unusual specimen of garnet before us as we write, as large as a hickory nut. Its three equal axes, on right angles to each other, are as perfect as though they had been patterned by the careful device of a skilled artist. Such a stone, shattered and ground, maintains that structure in the crushing process.

Again, the ruby always crystallizes on a hexagonal system, so when we crush, smash, and grind a specimen of a ruby in the process of research, we are delighted to find that it also maintains this basical structure in its minutest fragment. In other words, we have in the geometrical structure of the precious stone an argument for specific creation that intelligence must receive. Also because of this fidelity to its division, the precious stones may be used by man not only in the decoration of his person but for his industry as well. So a diamond, ground into dust, remains of value to man in his arts and crafts because it loses none of its structural peculiarity or hardness, and diamond dust is carefully gathered and preserved.

Geometry is a mathematical science, and the figures of geometry, being absolute, are to be derived only from intelligence in application to the solution of structure and planes. Accident and chance are ruled out as deciding factors in the formation of precious stones. That they are specific creations we see further when we note the fact that such apparently unrelated structures as diamonds, rubies, sapphires, beryls, carbuncles, and coal are all made of the same material! What accounts for the difference? In color and hardness, in value and worth, they are as different as chalk from cheese; yet they are made of the same material. The beryls, for instance, are themselves a large family, differing one from the other in beauty and worth. They may be pink, green, yellow, blue or white, and their hexagonal crystals often exhibit a beautiful twelve-sided double pyramid that is of marvelous design, but the beryl remains a beryl, — the same wherever and however found.

Of what use are they? They delight man, and with this their Creator seems to rest content. They appear frequently in the Scriptures as being associated with the future surroundings of redeemed man in the Eternal City; and it seems reasonable to suppose that if God is to surround us with their wonderful beauty in all eternity, we may enjoy their beauty for the present life, while we await that translation which shall convey us to their eternal presence.

I have a warm friend whom I admire tremendously, and who is a noted Bible teacher. He wears in his necktie a beautiful diamond that was given to him as a love-gift from a close friend. One day as he was riding on the train between appointments, a rather "nosey" woman said to him, "Doctor, what right have you as a Christian, and a child of God, to be wearing a diamond?" The doctor looked into her somewhat unpleasant countenance and replied courteously, "While I do not believe it concerns you, I will nevertheless answer your question. I am told by God in His Word, in Revelation the twenty-first chapter, verses nineteen to twenty-one, that the heavenly city I will some day inhabit has its foundations garnished with twelve manner of precious stones. Since I am to dwell for eternity surrounded by their blazing beauty, my Father has given me this small fragment of the heavenly foundation to wear here, that I may get used to the wonder of their beauty hereafter." The woman retired somewhat crestfallen and the doctor still wears his diamond to this day, as he is entitled to do.

Every color of the rainbow is here captured and made permanent for the delight of man, and the gem world is poetry and beauty made physical for our enjoyment.

When we have exhausted the contents of the rocks, which are the pantry shelves we are considering (if we ever can exhaust their contents!), we are faced with another gracious provision our mother's pantry could never equal. When the shelves are emptied, or if they contain nothing for our use, we then use the shelves themselves for purposes as essential as the contents they may have held! For these layers of rock, called strata, are as varied in their form and structure as is all the multiplicity of their varied content. One layer is granite, and with that we build our great buildings which weather the storms of the ages; another perhaps is made of marble, and with that we build our temples of worship, or from it carve the enduring statues and monuments which commemorate our great events or make tangible the artistic yearnings of our greatest dreamers. Again we find a layer of sandstone, used for every purpose from making sidewalks to sharpening knives and tools that need a perfect edge. Consider this for yourself; the subject is unlimited, and bears testimony to creation and forethought on the part of the Creator that all can appreciate. Verily our Lord Jesus spoke truth when He said, that if man should refuse to praise God the very rocks would cry out!

Rocks are frequently mentioned in the Scripture, the word itself appearing no less than one hundred and fifteen times in the Old and the New Testaments, and the word "stone" appearing almost four hundred times in addition to this. Often the word "rock" is used with the exact and specific connotations ascribed to that word in our modern vocabulary, but even though it is often used in this exact and literal sense, very frequently it has a symbolic and spiritual meaning as well.

It is natural that dwellers in a desert country, wanderers in a wilderness, and men who fought with the ancient means of bow, arrow and spear, should prize very highly the presence of rocks. To the jaded traveler on the heated sands, the presence of a towering rock, with the grateful shade it cast, seemed a special beneficence of Providence. So Isaiah writes of the coming Saviour and says ". . . He shall be as *the shadow of a mighty rock* within a weary land." Thus on the accepted fact of the comforting, refreshing influence of the rock in the desert, the prophetic description of the work of the Messiah is founded.

David, harassed and encompassed by his foes, fought with a heroism and courage rarely if ever equalled in all antiquity. Skilled in the use of weapons of defense, crafty in his strategy, almost invincible in fighting for a cause he knew to be just, this man had much to say about the value of a rock. To him it was a fortress, a place of safety and a never-failing defense. Two things he trusted in: the power of a great rock to shelter him while he fought his battles, and the power of his God to defend and protect him. So David wrote of God in the eighteenth Psalm: *"The Lord is my rock and my fortress,* and my deliverer; my God, my strength, in whom I will trust." He uses this same expression again in the thirty-first Psalm, "For thou art my rock and my fortress," and repeats this thought in similar terms occasionally, when he remembers the dangers through which he had been safely kept.

There is even an element of humor in one reiterated reference of David's as he remembers the combats of his youth. So often he said, "I will flee to a rock that is higher than I." David knew the inadequacy of a defense less than the height of his own stature. Had he backed up to a low rock to defend himself against his enemies with shield and sword, some one might have slipped around to his rear and, reaching over a low rock, smitten him on his unprotected head. So in moments of extremity this warrior-psalmist sought a rock that towered far above his own height. Thus also he felt that any conception of Deity that was adequate to his soul's need must consist of a towering being that was so high and far above humanity, that man could safely rest sheltered in His shadow.

We desire to suggest an interesting study to the reader. Take a concordance, and trace every appearance of the word "rock" in the Bible, noting all the occasions where it applies symbolically to the person of Deity. So we see in the Bible that the word "rock" occurs forty-two times, to signify the person of God and the Saviour, Jesus Christ. The reader will see that the men of old who were used of God to write the Scripture had a right to speak of the Creator as a Rock, for He used the term to apply to Himself. Thus in Isaiah the forty-fourth chapter, God speaks to the prophet and says: ". . . Is there a God beside me? Yea, there is no Rock, I know not any." On this authority, then, we say that the word rock frequently is a poetic synonym for God.

So also in the New Testament, the thought is vividly expressed by Jesus, in His remarkable conversation with Peter. The sixteenth chapter of Matthew contains the account, and tells us that the Lord questioned the disciples concerning the opinions men held regarding Him. They replied that some said that He was John the Baptist, others that he was Elijah, and still others said that He was probably Jeremiah or one of the prophets returned. (We note from this that *all* sensed that He was more than human, even the rabble seeking some explanation to account for His supernatural presence and power.) The Saviour then turned to Peter and said, *"But who do ye say that I, the Son of Man, am?"* And Peter replied, "Thou art the Christ, the Son of the Living God!" Jesus then answered him, "Blessed art thou, Simon, son of Jonah, for flesh and blood hath not revealed this unto thee, but my Father who is in heaven. And I also say unto thee, that thou art Peter (Greek, petros), and upon this rock (Greek, petra) I will build my church, and the gates of Hades shall not prevail against it."

Considerable misunderstanding has sprung up because of this verse, which would have been avoided if note had been taken of the difference in these two words in the Greek text. It has been contended by some that the Lord said He would build His church on Peter, but such is not the case. We have an interesting play upon words, to point the graphic lesson which the Saviour desired to teach. To Peter He said, "Thou art Petros . . ." A petros is a small stone, easily moved, like a pebble in a river bed. But the Lord continued, "upon this *petra* I will build my church . . ." A petra is a living rock, fixed, immovable, such as a crag, a cliff, or the granite wall of an eternal mountain. As an instance of the contrast here suggested, the great awe-inspiring cliffs of Yellowstone would be called "petra," while a small boulder swept along by the river below would be "petros."

Peter himself tells us that the Lord did not state that He would found the church on Peter the man. Peter is careful to show us this in his First Epistle, the second chapter and the paragraph beginning with the sixth verse. Here we are informed by Peter that the Rock on which the church was planted is Jesus Christ Himself, and in most unmistakable language he denies the present current tradition that he, the apostle, is in any sense the foundation. Poor Peter! Tossed about by emotion, ready to die for his Lord at one hour and denying Him the next, he was a "rolling stone" indeed. Not upon such a fallible and human foundation was the church to rest, but upon a living rock, fixed, immovable. What was that rock? Not Peter, nor Peter's confession, *but the fact that he confessed as a truth.* When Jesus said, "Who am I?" Peter replied, "Thou art the Christ, the Son of the Living God!", and Jesus said, "On *that* fact I will build my church."

Rocks are primarily for foundations. No wise man builds his house unless he has a foundation of stone, and if he has none he makes out of cement a stone base for his building. So our Lord tells the parable of the two men in the sixth chapter of Luke. One built his house upon the shifting sands, the other upon the rock. When the storm came and beat upon those two houses, the one resting upon the rock was unimpaired; but the house that was built upon the sands collapsed. Of course it did; and the amazing thing today is the fact that men who know enough to build a house in which to live their *natural* lives, always build it on the strongest foundation, and are at the same time content to build their *spiritual* lives on the shifting quicksands of man's changing philosophies.

It is because rocks are for foundations that Paul wrote in the third chapter of First Corinthians, ". . . as a wise master-builder I first laid a foundation . . . For other foundation can no man lay, save that which is laid, which is Christ Jesus." How odd it seems to contemplate the fact that men who would not even build a chicken coop without first laying a foundation, will drift along all their lives with no foundation for their living! We note here then, that Jesus is the Rock of which the Scripture speaks when it says ". . . and that Rock was Christ!" (First Corinthians 10:4).

What shall we say, then, concerning that Rock? Only what is written in Romans nine thirty-three, which states, "Behold, I lay in Zion a *stone of stumbling and a rock of offense,* and he that believeth on Him shall not be put to shame." To which Peter, speaking by the Holy Spirit, adds: "Behold I lay in Zion a chief corner-stone, elect, precious; and he that believeth on Him shall not be put to shame." This repetition is not without meaning, for there is certain and eternal shame for him who rejects Jesus Christ, and builds his life upon any other hope. So Peter continues, "For you therefore that believe is the preciousness, but for such as disbelieve, the stone that the builders rejected, the same was made the corner-stone, and a stone of stumbling, and a rock of offense, for they stumble, being disobedient to the word."

Here, then, is portrayed the dual nature of the work of Christ, still under the simile of the stone. More precious by far than any rare gem for which men sell their all, Jesus is prized by those He has saved. But to those who reject Him as Saviour (because they are disobedient to the Word of God and reject its truth, which we here seek to demonstrate), He becomes the Judge Who condemns. Grim as the grey granite of a vast penitentiary, and as inescapable, is this fact: *if we reject the Lord Jesus here, He must reject us hereafter!*

Daniel in his vision looked and saw a stone cut out without hands, which fell upon the Gentile world-dominion and ground it to powder. Then that stone grew and grew, until it filled the earth! Thus once again under the symbol of a stone, the fact of the return of Jesus Christ to rule and to reign is graphically presented. Not only in its testimony to the inspiration of Moses, and the accuracy of his revelation, does the *dry land* testify, but also to the fact of Him of Whom Moses wrote, do the *very stones speak.*

Botany and the Rose of Sharon

Genesis Chapter One:

11. And God said, Let the earth bring forth grass, the herb yielding seed, *and* the fruit tree yielding fruit after his kind, whose seed *is* in itself, upon the earth: and it was so.

12. And the earth brought forth grass, *and* herb yielding seed after his kind, and the tree yielding fruit, whose seed *was* in itself, after his kind: and God saw that *it was* good.

13. And the evening and the morning were the third day.

CHAPTER SIX

Botany and the Rose of Sharon

HAVING recounted in the previously quoted words of this divinely inspired paragraph of the formation of the oceans and the appearance of the dry land, Moses now continues the account with the words that face this chapter.

In such simple language as this does Moses cover the stupendous fact of vegetation, which is the first appearance, in his record, of *vitality*. It is to be noted that on the preceding days of creation nothing is mentioned or dealt with except inorganic matter. In that realm there is no growth, reproduction, change or mutation, but things remain as they originate, subject only to the law of degeneration. Granite decomposes, suffers erosion, and becomes in turn gravel, sand, dust, soil, but there are no infant granites being brought into being by the ancient rocks of this system! The plants are the first things to appear with the power of reproduction, and with the ability to multiply and possess new territory.

The whole round globe teems with the creatures of botany. What is the origin of this order of life? There are two answers which are in absolute opposition to each other, and cannot be reconciled. The Scriptures say that botany came in response to a fiat command of the omnipotent God, and thus is His creation. The materialist, or the naturalist philosopher does not agree with this, and says, instead, that botany is the result of the natural tendency to combination inherent in the particles of matter.

A very brief examination will convince the true scientist that the theory of naturalism must be rejected, *as particles of matter do not combine,* but on the contrary *they must be combined!* There is a world of difference here; the tendency

to combine would be a natural process if it existed, but particles that are combined demand direction, force, power,
supervision and, above all else, *intelligence!* It is apparent
on the face of the matter that we have here a clear case
for creation. There is no tendency inherent in matter to
form combinations. As an instance, nitrogen and oxygen will
combine, but only under certain circumstances and in obedience to force exerted. Under the influence of strong electric
currents this process will occur, and every laboratory worker
realizes the stubbornness of nitrogen in its natural state.
So the elements that make up the air we breathe are not a
combination, that is, their individuality is not lost by amal-
gamation.

Even the materialist knows in practice that elements will
not combine without some kind of active agent to force the
combinations; so he does not assemble on the dinner table
the elements of a meal, and then sit down and wait until
they combine themselves into a meal to satisfy his hunger.
He would starve to death while he waited! Instead, he gets
the elements already combined in an edible form by some
creature *which has been alive,* and there is no other kind of
food for man that will sustain his life indefinitely.

A tendency denotes a movement in a particular direction.
There is absolutely no such thing as a "tendency" to diversity, any more than there is dirty light, or dark light, or an
uphill declivity. These things are contradictions in terms,
and if the English language means anything, scientifically
at least, a tendency towards diversity is inadmissible; and
that the world of botany is diverse we see at a glance. Certain
fruits are composed of the same elements that comprise other
substances which are not fruit at all, but are vegetables.
Many fruits, diverse in taste, aroma, appearance, and flavor
are made out of the same elements; how, then, can we account
for this vast difference if the plants are all a result of a natural
tendency to combinations?

Combinations are common, but again we say they are specific. Sodium chloride is always salt; H_2O_2 is always peroxide of hydrogen, N_2O is always nitrous oxide, and if this were not so the science of chemistry would be impossible. But this so-called tendency of the naturalist seems to have studied Shakespeare, and its favorite motto seems to be, "To be, or not to be!" So the only way botany can settle this business of tendency is to obey the command of God as it is recorded by Moses, and reproduce only and always after its own kind!

Some two years ago I took my two boys to the upper waters of the San Joaquin River on a fishing trip after steel head salmon. When we made camp we discovered a field of watermelons across the road, and after a little chat with the owner we acquired (legally!) one of the biggest and best melons we had seen that year. Ten minutes later, back in camp, we were buried up to our ears in the aforesaid melon, when one of our camp neighbors came over and engaged my oldest boy in conversation. He said, "Boy, do you like watermelon?" My son replied, "Yes, sir. Did you ever see a boy who didn't?" The man smiled and said, "I suppose you know where that watermelon came from?" The lad said, "Yes, sir, God made it for us to enjoy." The fellow was an infidel, and his face turned brick-red with exasperation. He snorted, "Bah! God made nothing. That watermelon just came because of the nature of all plants. They desire to have seeds so that their kind will persist, and continue to exist. Get that fool idea of God out of your head; that melon came just so the plant would have a place to keep its seed in safety."

Before telling this awful creature what I thought of a grown man trying to wreck a child's faith in God, I waited to see what the lad would say. At first he looked puzzled, and then a slow grin came over his face and he said, "No, Mister, you are wrong. Wait a minute and I will show you why." He turned back into the tent, and quickly returned with a small gourd in his hand. It was about as big as a baseball, round, hard, and so tough that they had been bouncing it on a huge rock most of the time they had been playing with it. Holding this gourd up to the doubter the boy shook it, so that it rattled, and said, "Do you hear that? It's full of seeds; in fact it has more seeds in it than a watermelon. But this gourd is too tough to eat; it has no taste, no sugar, and no juice. These seeds are safe, so the plant will live again. The watermelon seeds will never grow, because the melon is so good to eat we pick it and throw the seeds into the garbage can! Now it seems to me that if the watermelon vine just wanted to make a holder for its seeds, it would not have wasted time making thirty or forty pounds of nice, sweet, juicy red meat that would tempt us to eat it, and to keep the plant from making use of the seeds. It would make a gourd or something else nothing could use. No, sir, I believe you are wrong; you can't explain a watermelon that way. God made it for us to enjoy, so if you will excuse me, I'll just go back to mine and enjoy it." The man went away muttering down his neck, saying something to the effect that you couldn't explain anything to a guy like that; and I agreed with him! Faith, plus intelligence, is able always to meet the silly reasoning of infidelity, even when that faith is in the heart of a child, and the intelligence only that of a lad.

Plants are all well-regulated machines, or perhaps a better figure would be to say that every creature of botany is a well-regulated chemical laboratory, functioning with amazing consistency. This we shall show later in this study; just now we desire only to note the fact that there is no machine without the inventor, who thinks it out and assembles it, and decides the power that operates it. We might again claim this as an equation in logic: machine equals inventor plus mechanic, which in turn equals intelligence applied, — Q.E.D.! There is no possibility of a chemical laboratory without an architect, a builder, and an operator to keep it functioning. Thus we seem to be brought up to the conclusion reached by Moses through the revelation that God gave him; namely, that the world of botany is the result of the creative power of God.

These statements of Moses in the opening paragraph are in perfect accord with the most exact conclusions of science. He says that the plants came before the animals, and that they were the first living things to grace this earth in the presently existing order. He further contends that botany is in three general divisions, the grasses, the herbs, and the trees. No established fact of any science is contrary to this conclusion, which was reached by revelation long before botany, as a science, was dreamed of.

Certainly, every intelligent person who has thought on this subject can clearly see that if the animals are to live on the plants, the plants *must* have preceded animals in origination, whether by creation or "by happenstance." This implies intelligence and forethought in provision for coming creatures that itself excludes the theories of chance by which men seek to displace the truth of the creation account, and we must accept the Mosaic record as logical.

The whole fabric of creation is started with the appearance of small botanical creatures called algae; and they are presumed to be the first life to appear, and to be still the lowest form of life in existence today. So whether we read the story in the text book of botany or in the inspired book of Genesis, the record is one of this fact, at least. How could Moses know? In that far-away day when the present sciences were not even dreamed of, Moses could not possibly have written by human knowledge a fact that the entire earth agrees with. Nowhere on the face of this planet can an exception be found to the clear and comprehensive facts of this simple statement; and a library of text books cannot say it with more understanding.

The creatures of the vegetable world express the fact of God's forethought in creation more than any other single realm of study. In the green and the growing thing there is abundant provision for all the needs of man in his complex life. Food is primarily a matter of botany; for even when we eat meat we are eating food which has been made possible because the animal that provided that flesh, in turn ate the green things, or ate some other creature that did eat the grass, and the leaves, and the seeds.

The houses we live in are made possible because of the trees that grew, and the coal that heats our homes is also the product of green plants that grew in the long ago. The very paper on which this is printed came from trees, and the suit that the average man wears is made of pure wool, at least half of which grew on a little bush down in Dixie! The structure of the tires we ride upon is fabric that came from a plant, and now even the silk stockings and the personal intimate garments we wear close to us are a vegetable product! Everywhere, from the linen napery that makes the table of civilized man so delightful a sight, to the giant tent that encloses the circus planned for his amusement, we are served by the creatures of botany.

We also note that in every climate there are green things which serve man specifically in that particular region. Where the deadly fevers abound the quinine bush is close at hand. In certain northern climes where their particular juices are needed the apples abound, but in the tropics, where apples are not so essential they will not thrive. In their place we have the banana and the mango, the papaya, and the other tropical fruits, too numerous to mention.

From this we see that the Creator designed certain creatures to match a specific climate, *and that they are not produced by their environment*. When a plant reaches the limit of the range within which it was designed to thrive, it does not adapt itself to the new climate, but perishes; unless it is artificially protected by the devices of man. For this reason we have in our temperate climates the familiar hothouse and conservatory, to make an artificial climate in which creatures that would otherwise perish, being out of their native realm, may exist for our pleasure. There are, of course, certain creatures which are more or less ubiquitous by nature and design. For instance, I do not know of any place, with the exception, of course, of the polar regions, where the humble bean will not grow. What a debt of gratitude man owes to the bean! Wildernesses have been conquered by its aid, wars have been won with its help, and even Boston is not too proud to be known as the city of beans!

It is evident, however, that many of our naturalists have not considered the implications of this fact or else have sought to avoid the inevitable conclusion. We remember a professor we had in college some twenty years ago who was an ardent evolutionist, and who often tried to prove the truth of that theory by saying that the environment produced the mutations which in turn produced the new species. He stated as one of his pet arguments, that a plant or an animal which reached the edge of its natural range would so change that it could no longer live in its original ancestral limits, and thus a new species would arise.

As an instance he cited the supposed fact of the Mexican hairless dog which is known as the Chihuahua Terrier. Many have seen this weird example of a dog, which no real dog lover even likes to call a dog! It belongs to that class of canines which should really be called "fur-bearing cockroaches," a type of useless poodles that women carry around with them when they are too lazy to carry a baby! The best description we ever heard of a Mexican hairless dog was by an old fellow who said, "It looks like thirty cents worth of spoiled liver, animated!" It does. It is a sad and discouraged blue, with certain blotches and mottled patches that make this description particularly apt.

It is as bald as an elephant. Being designed to dwell in tropical climates, it has no need of hair to cover it. The professor said that if one of these hairless dogs was transplanted to a colder northern climate, nature would protect the animal by covering it with hair. When this animal that has so changed his appearance gave rise to progeny in this rigid atmosphere, the progeny would all be covered with an adequate protection in the form of hair. When there had thus been produced a race of Mexican "hairless" dogs that were no longer hairless, we would have an example of evolution in operation.

At this point in the demonstration, we had the poor grace to laugh, and the instructor asked us what was so funny.

We told him!

A few years before this class room episode, we were working in a northern concern in the lumber industry. One of the wood bosses went south during a brief vacation, and when he came back he brought with him a wife. This woman had a pair of these Mexican hairless dogs which she valued highly, and they were the wonder of that whole northern region, as they were the first ever seen in that vicinity.

The dogs got along well through the heat of the summer, but when the cold winter started in, it was a different story. Did they sprout hair to keep them warm? They did not! They shivered and shook and suffered with the cold, until their owner knitted them each a warm woolen jacket with four legs, and aided them in that way. This sufficed for a short while, as long as they could lie beside the fire, but when the first snow fell one of the poor little brutes died of pneumonia! His mistress then put *both* of the woolen jackets on the sole survivor, but two weeks later he also died of pneumonia, in spite of the double protection!

When we told this to the professor he was somewhat chagrined, and we were careful to point out to him that while the dogs in his hypothetical demonstration were getting their hair they would perish and have no progeny. He said he had been unfortunate in his illustration, but the principle was true, nevertheless! *The whole world of living things,* however, testifies to the fact which *the plants enunciate so forcefully;* namely, that the Creator has designed each creature for the climate in which He caused it to dwell.

Adequately to cover the scope of this subject, volumes would be necessary, and it is not our intention to deal with it exhaustively. We desire only to illustrate the scientific accuracy of Moses, who contends for specific creation, and to cite the knowledge of scientific facts possessed by this generation, which show Moses to have spoken by inspiration. We will look in detail at some of the facts he records and some of the evidences in the various divisions he covers.

Moses starts his record with the mention of grass. The amazing manner in which grass, the absolute essential to animal life, covers the earth, has been commented on many times, not only by the scientist, but by the layman as well. It seems that wherever there is soil enough to sustain roots, grass comes into possession of that bit of dry land. Quietly, humbly, with no shout of marching forces or display of banners, but with power sufficient to cleave the stoutest stone and to lift and spread concrete sidewalks, the grass conquers where it is left alone to work its will. Of grasses, there are more than three hundred genera, and something over five thousand species have been enumerated by various schools of botany.

All are good for food for some creature or another, being amazingly well equipped to convert the invisible powers of sunlight into chemical constituents, and to organize, concentrate, and make these elements accessible to animals as food. While they live they are working to this end. Every spear-like blade, designed to pierce the soil, offers minimum resistance to the wind-pressure, and at the same time absorbs the utter maximum of chemical power from the light, and shouts the fact of *design*. From the instant that the grass springs into being, the whole plant works, root and blade alike, to fulfill its function in obedience to the commands of God Who created it. Even when it is dead its elements continue to act for our benefit, and dead grass is a valuable factor in the rejuvenation of the soil, fertilizing it so that other grasses can grow.

Even in the color of grass the benevolence of the Creator is seen. It is a known fact that certain colors have very marked effects upon the psychological reactions of the human being. Red is a color that irritates the entire nervous system, but green has the opposite effect. It is the most soothing color in the spectrum. The man who is surrounded by soft shades of green is apt to be mentally calm, even-tempered, and able to control his nervous reactions better than the man who is subject to the harsher influences of some other colors. It may be that this can account for the even temper of the American farmer, even in the face of such awful trials as Congressional attempts to help him solve his problems! But seriously speaking, can you imagine the nervous effect of nature upon man if God had been pleased to make the grass red instead of green?

To every creature of the world of botany certain individual powers and uses have been given, but there are certain functions and organizations that are common to all of them. Thus we see that all the plants have *roots,* which no other order of life can be said to possess. What an amazing and ingenious device the root is! Two functions are performed by this perfect arrangement, the first being mechanical. It is to be noted that every plant that protrudes above the surface of the soil must resist a terrific wind pressure, and the weight of that pressure is in exact proportion to the size of the plant above the soil.

The first function of the roots, then, is to anchor and balance the plant, and to act as a retaining structure in the face of stress. In the same fashion the intelligent engineer buries a log that he calls a "dead man" to anchor his towering poles, and afford an anchor to hold them upright when the pressure of the wind becomes too great. The construction of a suspension bridge follows this same principle. The length of the span determines upon a mathematical ratio the size and weight and depth of the anchor to which the mighty cables are fastened. If this manifests intelligence on the part of the engineer, why should the same conclusion be wrong when applied to the Creator?

It may further be noted that design has arranged that the root-system of the plant or tree is in accordance with the shape and size of the tree, the need in each individual case being exactly met by the provision for that need. Thus, a tall tree that towers far up into the air has a deep root which goes far down into the soil to afford a counter-balance against that height. Another tree, having a wide spread of branches, will have a root-system that spreads out under the soil so as almost to duplicate the shape of the tree above the soil, and thus compensate for the wind pressure of that specific individual. What marvels of design are here seen by the inquiring mind of intelligent man!

The second and even more important function of the root is to feed the plant. The plant is a chemical device that assembles and transmutes certain elements into food, and the work is done by the leaves and roots. The termini of the roots are tiny thread-like particles called rootlets, and these are the "mouths" of the plant. Out of the soil these rootlets take the chemical elements that the parent plant needs, and they never make a mistake! How many students of chemistry make this proud boast; that they never made a mistake all their lives, nor confused one chemical with another! This, however, the roots can truthfully claim. If it is potassium that particular plant requires, potassium is what the root chooses out of all the elements of the soil. If it is nitrogen, then the root takes nitrogen. So absolute is the chemical knowledge apparently possessed by these roots, that the roots of twenty different species may all be tangled in one indistinguishable mass, yet each tiny spongiole will invariably choose from the many chemical elements available just those required by the parent plant.

At the same time that the roots are performing this function in the soil, the leaves are functioning as the "lungs" of the plant. Not only does the plant "breathe" by means of the leaves, but these leaves also have power to take out of the atmosphere invisible matter conveyed by the rays of the sun, and apply these to the problem of plant production. Certain food values are put into the plant by the light, as well as by the food it gets from the soil. Thus an amazing and ingenious machine functions all through the life of the plant, for the benefit of man and beast alike. These things we all know, of course; but how many of us ever pause to note in these facts the wonderful proof of specific creation, to which they so ably testify?

When we turn to the division of plant life we call the flowers, we are once more faced with a perfect proof of design and creation. Flowers are common to all plant life, from grass to the tallest trees. There must be flowers before there can be fruit or seeds, and there is no more fruitful or profitable sphere of study for the scientist than that offered by the flowers. They introduce to us, for instance, the color question. Where did the stupendous variations of color in the flowers originate?

The materialist, as usual, is ready with a naturalistic reason, and to him the question of color in flowers is no mystery. He appreciates the fact that is apparent to all: the aid of insects, and particularly of bees, is very valuable to the blossoms, in the process of fertilization. So the mechanistic philosopher tells us glibly that the flowers "invented" color to attract the bees! We were taught this in college, as you were, and we have both read it in books innumerable since we left the class room.

We were always impressed with the weakness of this explanation, from the time we first heard it, as we assumed that invention was a process exclusive to intelligence, and much as we love flowers we cannot admit this implication, that they have the power of abstract reasoning! The question is now out of the realm of the abstract, and into the sphere of scientific demonstration at last. To show how lacking in truth this theory of the materialist is, it has recently been demonstrated that bees are color blind, and cannot tell one color from another!

The poor flowers! After all their trouble, inventing colors to attract the bees, it is now known that a bee can't tell blue from pink, or green from purple, black from yellow! Is there, then, no reason for colors in the blossoms? Indeed there is; the creationist sees a reason for every act his God has performed, and is not content to rest his inquiry until he has discovered that use. Thus our knowledge of creation grows, and with our growing knowledge comes an enhanced appreciation of the Creator.

The physicist knows that color is a phenomenon connected with the speed and length of vibrations of light through the atmosphere. There is also a difference in the heat factor and refraction of the various colors, and all this enters into the problem of color in the flower. Each blossom is colored to attract to the parent plant just the amount of heat and the kind of light-rays the plant needs, and here is a very specific and material reason for these colors. So intricately is the problem inter-related, that the amount of heat-elements the plant gets is determined by the flower's color, and this also assures that shade of color in the next crop of flowers, so that the process may be continued, to the lasting benefit of the plant.

In the flower is also found the beauty and the mystery of sex. Some are male and some are female, but the vast majority have both male and female organs in the one blossom. The male organ is called the stamen, and it produces the fertilizing element. The female organ is called the pistil, and it contains the seed-germ, from which there develops the seed or the fruit. Thus, logically and necessarily, the male organ, the stamen, is higher in the blossom stalk, so that when the fertilizing element, the pollen, drops, it may be caught by the stigma below and conveyed to the ovaries of the blossom. But in the dropping blossoms, like the fuchsia, which hang upside down, the position is reversed, so that the pistil is on the top of the blossom and the stamen is beneath. Thus when the law of gravity causes the pollen to drop earthward, it still falls on the female organ and the process of reproduction is consummated in the habitual manner.

This is absolute evidence of design, as are the many and varied methods used to cause the pollen to fall. In some plants this work is carried on by insects, in others a certain arrangement of cilia will make the sensitive column that carries the stamen and the pistil jerk from side to side with spasmodic motion, so that the pollen is shaken loose. Some of these mechanisms are so delicately adjusted that the breath of a passing breeze will be sufficient to set them in motion, and we have seen this process operate at the touch of a tiny ant!

The entire purpose of the blossom seems to be consummated in the production of the seeds, and the flowers seem to be endowed with a close substitute for mother-love in their tender care of the developing seeds. They seem to know just how much sunshine the baby seeds need, and some of them, like the sunflower, will follow the sun all the way across the heavens in his diurnal journey to assure a sufficient supply. So the blossom that faces the east in the morning will face the south at noon, and be looking west, straight at the descending sun, at the moment it sets beneath the horizon. Many of them further protect the seeds by closing up when the rain begins, to defend the seeds from the effects of moisture. Among this latter class is the well-known portulaca, which every California child knows so well. It is the best barometer in the vegetable kingdom, and always closes up about a half hour before it begins to rain. When I was a lad I early discovered that fish bite in the rain, so I kept my eye on the portulaca during the summer vacations. When the flowers began to close I grabbed my can of worms and fishing-pole, and over the back fence I went! I went out the *back way* because if I went out the front mother would see my fishing-pole, and go look at the portulaca! She knew as well as I did, or better, that the blossoms knew, and she had many funny ideas against boys fishing in the rain! "Fewer fish and less pneumonia" seemed to be her motto.

Flowers are the poor man's gems. He may not be able to afford the rare and scintillating jewels with which the very rich may bedeck their persons, but for him the blossoms reproduce every shade and variety of color that is found in the precious stones. They are the most exquisite earthly things, and at the price of ten cents for a packet of seeds, the poorest of men may have a treasury of brilliant hues. And even though the man may be so poor that he cannot afford the price of a single package of seeds, he can still walk abroad in the woodlands and the meadows, and drink deep of the beauty that the Lord has so freely provided.

They are not only exquisite in color, shape, and form, but in structure as well. It may have been intended as a poetic reference when the Lord Jesus Christ said, "Consider the lilies of the field, how they grow; they toil not, neither do they spin; yet I say unto you that Solomon in all his glory was not arrayed like one of these;" but it was also a true scientific observation. It is absolute truth, as was every word that fell from His lips.

Solomon's choicest robe was a silken one of purple hue. To the eye of man it was gorgeous, perfect. But put it under the "eye" of a modern microscope, and its texture changes to a coarse rope-like structure, spotted here and there with patches of color. What the eye sees as perfection is thus shown to be faulty and course in the extreme. Put under the same instrument the petal of a lily of the field, such as purple iris, and the more it is magnified the more beautiful and perfect it appears! In very truth, no human that ever lived was arrayed in such perfection as characterizes the lilies of the field. The flowers are God's evidence of His existence and of His activity in creation, and so long as they live and bloom this earth will not be without witness of Him.

After the blossoms, there come the seeds, and they also are an able witness to the fact of specific creation. Our Lord calls attention to their fecundity when He states that some of the "good seed" brought forth sixty, seventy, and a hundred fold. Were this not so there would be no science of agriculture, no business of farming, and no food for man. If the farmer got only one or two seeds back for every one he planted, where would his increase come in? But the very thought of planting and growing is bound up in the companion thought of increase, and the two are inseparable.

The archenemy of childhood (castor oil), which is so often a blessing in disguise, comes from a bean that reproduces with about fifteen hundred per cent increase. A sunflower will reproduce four thousand seeds from one seed that is planted, and sweet corn much more than that. The land area of the entire United States is about three million, seven hundred forty-three thousand, three hundred forty-four square miles; but if we saved and planted all the progeny of one grain of corn, in three years we could have enough to plant the entire United States, as thickly as corn is ordinarily planted by the farmer in his fields. No wonder God said, "It is good." As a device to assure the feeding of many creatures, can man's ingenuity beat it?

Equally intriguing to the student of the evidences of creation are the methods that the seeds use for wide distribution. To the plants have been given the task of subduing the face of the earth, and they are everlastingly at their task. The common cockle-bur is a case in point. In every seed pod of this plant there are two seeds, and when the pod falls to the ground only one of them springs up that year. Thus the plant is assured of continuity throughout the second year, even if the first year crop is a failure, for seed number two normally comes up in the second year of its life. But in case the new plant that comes from seed number one is cut down, burned or otherwise destroyed *before the plant comes to seed,* number two springs right up into life without waiting for the second year. Who tells number two when it is time to sprout? Where is the alarm-clock that always goes off at the right hour, and which nobody has to wind? The method of the cockle-bur would be a worthy thing for wheat to emulate, or corn, oats, barley or any other grain that the farmer raises for a food crop. We remember, however, that when God cursed the soil He said, "Thorns and thistles shall it bear . . ." and the thorny cockle-bur is equipped to carry out this mandate.

So we note also that the burdock has hooks to catch a ride on any object that may be passing, and this plant can thus increase its range and conquer more and more new territory. The thistles and the dandelions equip their seeds with parachutes to ride upon the winds to new dwelling places, and all of us who have walked through the beautiful fields of beloved Dixie in the autumn days know what it is to come back covered with "beggar lice," and by picking them off where we stop, help the plant to reach out for new soil in which to root its progeny. There are also seeds that are equipped with a glue which dries more or less quickly, and lacking hooks with which to hold on to man or beast, they yet have a means of adhering to the unwitting carrier. When they have clung a certain length of time the glue dries, and loses its power of adhesion, and right there the seed drops to plant a new outpost in the battle for extended range. Thus the green creatures of the world of botany had mastered the science of crop-rotation before it was dreamed of by the modern school of agriculture.

This line of evidence is practically unlimited, so as a concluding evidence of design we will cite the case of the cocoanut. This strange but delightful fruit grows near the shoreline of the briny sea, and when the ripe fruit falls, generally aided by the tropical hurricane or the sudden gale, it is apt to fall into salt water. It is therefore provided with an impenetrable husk, which is tough and tenacious, varnished to protect the surface, and light enough to float the seed contained within. After days of voyaging on the restless seas, the little craft is finally left by the receding tide high up on some beach, perhaps far away from the parent tree. Deep within the husk there is a hard, brittle nut, containing the elements of a new tree. As soon as this hull is covered with sand to the depth of about one-third, the nut begins to sprout, or to germinate.

Now it is essential that the germinating seed shall have moisture, and salt water will most decidedly not do. So the nut has within its hollow structure about a half pint of sweet fluid, and this is enough to keep the budding tree alive until it is rooted deeply enough for the rains to help provide the moisture needed. What astounding design is seen here. By this means the islands of the sea have gradually been conquered by the cocoanut palm, until there is scarcely a group of islands in the tropical regions that does not have its clump of trees. It is good for shelter, food and drink for the desert traveler who may chance that way. Design is so evidenced here, that it is unnecessary even to pause and point it out to the intelligent reader.

So God, at the end of this Third Day, looked at all His work and said of the world of botany, "It is good." What reasoning being can refuse to agree with that divine commendation? It *is* good.

It is good for food. In some varieties we find nourishment in the leaves, some feed us by their roots, others by their stalks and of some we eat all three. It is good for shelter, so the desert traveler erects himself a house of canvas for the temporary abiding place of the night. It is good to heal the sick and suffering body of man, for a vast majority of our healing drugs come from the creatures that are in the realm of botany. In a very definite sense of the word all healing is divine healing. The Bible consistently maintains all through its marvelous revelations that Jesus Christ was the source, channel, and means of creation. John specifically states, "By Him were all things made and without Him was not anything made that was made." In the world of botany there are various powers and properties which have a healing influence upon the suffering bodies of humanity. These properties must have been imparted to these growing things at the time of their creation. If the Lord Jesus has incorporated in some botanical creature, drugs that heal the body of men when used by human intelligence, who then is the ultimate healer? Healing that is derived from materia medica, which in turn has been distilled from some plant that God created, is just as divine as is other healing that comes as an answer to prayer.

The references to this order of life that are met with in the Scripture are many and varied. The Holy Spirit has taken more illustrations from the plants and their kin, to illuminate divine teaching, than from any other order of life. It is a fascinating study that the reader would do well to pursue, tracing the various plants, shrubs, fruits, grains, and trees all through the Bible, and counting how many times each is mentioned. This will lend a dignity to the work of this creative period that many readers now fail to appreciate.

So Peter says, "All flesh is as grass, and the glory of man is as the flower of grass." In the face of eternity, man's brief day is as the life span of the flowers that bloom so short a period on the grass in the field: "All flesh is as grass." Like the grass we must fade away and die; yet grass somehow lives again! In the new substance of a higher form of life the dead grass ascends and arises to a newness of life, and all flesh is as grass.

Again our Lord says, "I am the vine, ye are the branches." What a priceless illustration that is! Separate the branch from the vine, and the branch will die. Take away all the branches, and no vine is left. We note also that fruit always comes on the branches, never on the trunk of the tree or the vine. Did you ever see apples growing on the trunk of the tree, or grapes growing on the trunk of the vine? This is also our Lord's graphic manner of telling us that if we do not bear fruit for Him, then there is no fruit in the Christian kingdom. This also explains the inner meaning of the Saviour's statement: "Every branch in me that beareth not fruit, He taketh it away." In our great California vineyards, we know that the old branches must be pruned back every year to insure a crop the following season. But when the old branch is removed, the smaller portion of it is allowed to remain, two buds being the general rule. From these two buds on the old branch there spring two new branches, and it is on these new branches that the fruit appears. So the Lord said, "Every branch in me that beareth not fruit, He *pruneth back* . . . ," and that is a message of hope and aspiration, not of despair for past failures.

The very humblest plants in the vegetable kingdom enter into the Scripture record,—even the tiny plant that clings to the old decaying walls of Palestine, called the hyssop. Associated with the life of sinful man by attachment to his very dwelling places, the hyssop was used to sprinkle the blood of sacrifice, and thus to share in the ceremony of redemption and cleansing from the stain of sin. John the apostle tells us in his account of the crucifixion, that the sponge of vinegar was offered to the dying Redeemer upon a bough of hyssop, thus linking in this action the ancient ceremonies of expiation with the death of the Son of God, Who was the vicarious sacrifice for all men everywhere who believe on Him.

Flowers also enter into the blessed Book, for Jesus is called the "Lily of the Valley," and to Him is ascribed all the sweetness and beauty of that entrancing bloom. Quiet, modest and pure in color as the driven snow, it is yet so pervasive it fills the environment by its very inherent fragrance. It delights the eye of the most fastidious, it pleases the every sense of the beauty lover, it makes us feel closer to the God Who created it. But the most poetic and pleasing name that is ascribed to the Lord Jesus Christ is perhaps the "Rose of Sharon." This synonym for the Saviour has found its way into song, poetry, and story until every child in Christian homes associates it with Him, Who is the fulfillment of all this picture language suggests.

What is a rose? It is a creation of God that He designed and endowed with power to take the unseen beauty of the heavenly light of the sun, and make it visible to the human eye. Also it has the power to capture the elusive fragrance of the ethereal atmosphere and condense it into sweet perfume to delight the soul of man. So Jesus, the "Rose of Sharon," was incarnated to walk among men, and to bring to them in visible form all the beauty and light of God, and to distill among us the fragrance of heaven itself. He Who was God became man, that He might make the invisible Father real to us, and by His very presence set us yearning for the scenes of splendor, beauty, and glory in that home He has prepared for those who love Him.

The grass and the herb, the shrub and the vine, the fruit and the flower all testify to God's grace. And not these alone, but the trees and the seeds as well. Of the trees we mention only two; the first the "tree of life," which is said in the Bible to grow by the side of the river that flows forth from the throne of God. Our first parents were privileged to see that tree, for we read that after they sinned and fell they were ejected from the garden, "lest," said Jehovah, "they should eat of the tree of life and live forever." What a strange and divine contrast is this; — sinning man, in the first book of the Bible, cast out of Paradise lest he eat of the tree of life and live forever; and the forgiven, redeemed sinner in the last book of the Bible, freely invited to eat of this same tree that he *may* live forever! What this tree of life may be we cannot say, but since its leaves are said to be for the healing of the nations, and as it bore twelve manner of fruits, we presume it is a type or picture of the Lord Jesus. That it is a literal tree we are constrained to believe from the various references made to it in the Book; but as to its genus, species, and variety we cannot, of course, even speculate, as it is of Heavenly, not earthly, growth.

The second tree we mentioned here is the gaunt, repellent, two-limbed object that crowned the hill called Calvary; on which the Son of God died for the sins of the world. Behold, what manner of love is this! Behold, also, the Fruit hanging thereon, the strangest that ever graced a tree since time began! No bud and no blossom presaged the coming of the Fruit, for the limbs on which He hung were long since dead; and the Fruit hung there to suffer and die. Here, then, is love unfathomable; the sinless, perfect Son of God dying in agony for sinful, degraded sons of men. Why? That the justice of God which said, "The soul that sinneth, it shall die!" might be satisfied, and the mercy and love of God be free to operate and save the sinner. For the fruit which ripened on Calvary's tree in that tragic hour, let us thank God from the depth of our souls.

It may be understood in the light of the statement the Lord made in the days of His flesh, when He used even the humble seeds to typify His redeeming grace. To wondering men He said, "Except a corn of wheat shall fall in the ground and die, it abideth alone." This, then, was the fulfillment of that parable in which He then spoke; He died as a corn of wheat. But forth from the ground in which He was laid He came in power and triumph, like the wheat, to bring life to all men, and satisfy the hunger of hearts and souls.

See, then, how the world of botany praises God! The sea, the dry land, the green grass, and the tallest trees, they all cry aloud that Moses was right, when he said that they are the results of the creative power of an omnipotent God. Like all the creatures of God, save sinning man alone, they unite to sing His praises, to do His will gladly, and to function for the purposes for which He created them. Not only do they testify that Moses, who knew none of these facts that science has now confirmed, was right in all he wrote; but they challenge us with a clarion call to join in with all the creation in the worship and praise of creation's God.

Astronomy and the Bright and Morning Star

14. And God said, Let there be lights in the firmament of the heaven to divide the day from the night; and let them be for signs, and for seasons, and for days, and years;

15. And let them be for lights in the firmament of the heaven to give light upon the earth: and it was so.

16. And God made two great lights; the greater light to rule the day, and the lesser light to rule the night: *He made* the stars also.

17. And God set them in the firmament of the heaven to give light upon the earth.

18. And to rule over the day and over the night, and to divide the light from the darkness: and God saw that *it was* good.

19. And the evening and the morning were the fourth day.

CHAPTER SEVEN

Astronomy and the Bright and
Morning Star

THE consensus of opinion has always agreed with the statement of the Psalmist David, "The heavens declare the glory of God, and the firmament showeth His handiwork!" Poet and plowman, astronomer and artisan, civilized and savage have alike agreed that there is a testimony in the fact of the heavens that reason cannot refute. From the remotest ages man has been awed by the starry skies, and has sensed that they tell a tale of might and power far beyond the scope of human reason. Paul the apostle also said that the visible things of creation testify to the invisible Creator, and there is no voice that speaks so strongly and so universally as the voice of the stars and the planets.

So clearly is the voice of astronomy heard in its testimony to creative power, that many of the ancient peoples deified the heavenly orbs. Sun, moon, and stars alike have borne many names in the pantheons of antiquity. Even the children of Israel were not free from the taint of idolatry when they neglected their law and turned away from God's Word. The awe and amazement with which men have ever viewed the shining galaxy above but reiterates these words that David has spoken.

The phrase that David used is in the Hebrew language, "maaseh yadayim," and this seems to be the only place in the text of the Hebrew Bible where it occurs. It means literally "the work of the fingers," and may be translated somewhat freely by the common English term "fancy work." It may be compared to knitting, crocheting, tatting, or any sort of fancy work that may be used to occupy the fingers in idle moments.

We would not judge the character, worth, and ability of a woman by the sort of fancy work she does, and in the same sense the writer of the Psalm suggests that mighty and majestic as the works of God in the heavens may be, they are still not the measure of the scope and limit of His vast power. "In an idle moment," suggests the verse, "God crocheted the heavens and flung them out into space as an evidence of His power in creation." They have been so received from the time man first gazed in awe upon their majestic splendor and uncountable numbers.

It is with this sphere of creation, then, that Moses deals in the paragraph describing the works of God on the Fourth Day of Creation. We have read the paragraph of the first chapter of Genesis, verses 14 to 19, that deals with this event, but we will pause a moment to consider certain suggestions that have been made about these words, and also some that arise from the perusal thereof. Moses begins this day and its work in his characteristic fashion: "And God said, let there be . . ." The word is "lights" in the English translation, but in the Hebrew, as we have elsewhere noted, it is "ma-or," which means luminary, or light holder, light container. This statement is in direct contrast and opposition to what Moses had been educated to believe, in the schools of learning in the land of Egypt. We may pause to state that this is a somewhat common experience; many of us have to cast aside what we have been taught in schools of human wisdom when we hear the voice of God, and read the words of inspiration!

"Moses," says the Scriptures, "was learned in all the wisdom of the Egyptians." One of the sciences in which the schools of Egypt specialized was that of astronomy. This was natural, due to the prevalence of astrologers, diviners, soothsayers, and magicians at the royal court, many of whom depended upon the heavenly bodies for their methods and technique of forecasting the future. The pharaohs were learned men in their day, and Moses had received a royal education. Indeed, so well is this fact established, that the critic has suggested that Moses got most of his information from Egyptian sources, instead of from God.

This statement of Moses thoroughly refutes this falsehood. He calls the heavenly bodies the light containers, and the Egyptians held otherwise. It is not possible even in the advanced state of archaeological research to state definitely who were the first people to inhabit the land of Egypt. It is generally presumed that some Asiatic tribe first settled therein, but the culture of the Egyptians of biblical times was derived from an earlier people and was but an elaboration of their simpler ideas. Many weird and fantastic theories concerning the heavenly bodies formed a large part of the Egyptian knowledge, in all of which Moses was learned. To the religiously minded Egyptians, these stars had minds and personalities and partook somewhat of the nature of minor deities. Flaming chariots speeding across the skies may have intrigued the human wisdom of the man Moses. But when he came to write, guided by the inspiration of the Holy Spirit, he was careful to set forth the simple truth of the matter: namely, that the sun is the source of the light, as are also the stars, which in turn are other suns. He is also careful to differentiate between the stars and the satellites, and makes no errors here.

In the first verse of this chapter, Moses puts the planets in their proper place and order in creation. He says that God made the heavens, and then the earth. As the earth is a satellite of the heavenly orb, the sun, this must have been of necessity the order of creation. The sun may have been the parent of this planet, as some astronomers claim; but whether this is true or not, Moses makes no error here. Thus he seems to anticipate and shatter in advance the other principal objection of the critic, who says that Moses is scientifically wrong in putting light on the first day, and the sun is not created until the fourth day.

Even at the risk of possible repetition, we must deal here with this objection, and point out clearly that Moses does not state that these heavenly bodies are created on this fourth day of which he now writes. He does not use the Hebrew word "bara" (to create) in this entire passage, but uses instead the alternate expression, "asah" (to release from restraint). Up to this day the earth, emerging as a rehabilitated place prepared for the reception and life of strange and new orders of living things, has been shrouded in a vaporous blanket that causes the light to seep through in a wan and cheerless manner.

Such gloomy days are common even yet. How many times have we been in some seaport city at the hour of high noon, and have groped our way across the streets in danger of life and limb because of the fog that obscured the landscape, and imperiled traffic. Even those who have never been there, are familiar with the denseness of a London fog, made proverbial by its constant recurrence and impenetrable denseness.

It is evident in the Mosaic account of creation, that the first three days of creation were like that. The pall of night was lightened by the pallid gleam of a pale dawn, as the earth rolled on her endless journey of spinning upon her own axis. The black darkness of grim night gave way to the more cheerful light of a foggy day, and this light alleviated the landscape until night once more reigned supreme.

But to paraphrase this word for the sake of clarity, on this fourth day God spoke and said, "Let the light containers be released from restraint . . ." and the wonder of our present order occurred. The fog and vapor melted away, and the atmosphere was cleared of its hindering mist. Then for the first time the planet was gladdened with the now common miracle of the sunrise in all its visible splendor. Over the rim of the distant hills there was born a rosy glow that deepened soon to a golden hue, too bright for the eye of man to look upon, had there been a man to see. Like a living flame the first rays of the sunlight fell directly upon the planet, and the world of botany, born the preceding day, rejoiced and was glad. For twelve hours the sunlight remained to bless and warm the earth, then it began to fade in the distant west. The sky began to burn with living fire, and the Divine Artist flung His colors across the canvas of the blue dome above, as the first sunset died in a riot of splendor.

This order has continued ever since. So familiar, too, have the phenomena of sunrise, sunshine, and sunset become that we can scarcely realize that there was a day when all this began. If we dwelt upon the planet Jupiter, however, we could more clearly understand. Jupiter is sometimes called the "Fourth Day Planet," because this condition of vaporous obscurity prevails there even now. The direct rays of the sun do not penetrate to the face of that planet, and so far as science can say, they never have. It may well be, however, that some day this mist will be dissipated from the face of Jupiter, and the sun will shine through. If Jupiter were inhabited (which it is not), the people there might well cry out with wonder at their first sight of the sun, and say it was a new creation. But it is not, as it has been shining out in space for many ages past.

So Moses here notes only the new order. The light holders are on this day of creation made visible, and begin to function *for this planet,* as God had established and ordained that they should. What amazing accuracy is here displayed by Moses, who is thus far in absolute accord and agreement with the modern science of astronomy!

Certainly no modern man will contradict the statement of Moses that these heavenly bodies are to serve a useful purpose, aside from their testimony and amazing beauty. Moses states that the stars are to be for signs and seasons. Let us first note the accuracy of this observation, and then later inquire into the source of his knowledge. That the stars are signposts in nature we all agree.

The science of navigation would be impossible without the aid of the heavenly bodies. When the storms and the mists obscure the heavens for a sufficient period of time, even the ablest navigator is lost. By the use of his instruments, the navigator "shoots the sun" and determines his position on the boundless deep. At night the stars in their splendor keep him on his course, and the heavenly orbs are signs to the traveler, by sea or by land.

We have often chuckled over the humorous predicament of the captain of a small sailing vessel who made a voyage with one green hand. Alert and willing as are all the Irish, this embryonic sailor was induced to steer the schooner the first night at sea. Before retiring to his cabin below, the captain pointed to a star and said to his amateur helper, "Keep that star right in front of your mast and you will be on the course. If anything happens call me."

Some time later he was awakened by a pounding on the deck and he hastily arose to see what the trouble might be. As he thrust his head up the companionway, the Irish sailor called buoyantly, "I say, captain, pick me out another star, we passed that one!"

There have perhaps been other people both before this man and since, who thought that they had gone beyond the signs and portents that God had set for their guidance, but like this simple fellow, they were merely off their course. If men do follow the stars, they have guides that never waver.

They are signs to the farmer as well. When certain constellations flame in the sky, we know that the spring has come, and it is time to hasten the planting that later there may be the seasonal harvest. When the later orbs appear the man of wisdom knows it is too late to plant any but the hardiest species, for the winter is on the way. So the present age relies on such helps as the almanac and astronomy can give us in the forecast of the seasons, and we faithfully obey the signs in the heavens so that we may know when to plant, that we may later eat.

In one of his inimitable and happy series of essays, the famous David Grayson tells how he planted potatoes. His neighbors all told him that he had to plant in a certain time of the moon. David Grayson, however, went out each day and spaded up the earth. As long as the ground felt cold and clammy to his hand, he refused to plant. But the first time that the earth felt warm and moist, he sowed his crop in spite of the fact that the moon was not just right. He reports with some enjoyment that he had a crop two weeks before his neighbors, and concludes the episode with the humorous comment, "I farm the earth, not the moon." Nevertheless, it still remains true that in our latitudes at least, when winter's constellations are flaming in the sky, we do not sow our seed.

When Moses states that the heavenly bodies determine also by their appearance the days, the years, and the seasons, he is accurate in his statement. The day is determined by the fact of the earth's diurnal revolution *in the face of the sun*. Did Moses in that day of ignorance, when men believed that the earth was flat, and that the sun was spinning around the earth, possess our modern knowledge of the shape and rotation of this planet? Or did the Spirit of God inspire Moses to speak modern scientific truth here, as elsewhere? We will let the reader answer for himself. The fact remains, however, that Moses was accurate once again, and stated the fact as it is scientifically proved and believed today.

If his writings were not inspired, he must have known also, in that far-away age when nobody else dreamed it, that the earth not only revolves on her axis every twenty-four hours, but is also engaged in her ceaseless flight on a vast orbit about the sun. For Moses also states that these vast luminaries in the sky are to control the seasons. They do. Summer and winter, springtime and fall, year after year they come in their exact order as the earth in her journey through space assumes a certain definite position in regard to all the other planets, the sun, and even the far-away stars that gleam so dimly in boundless space. They are truly for signs and for seasons, for days and for years. Moses had made no mistake so far, but is remarkably in accord with the best and most recent findings of the science of astronomy, of which he could have had no personal knowledge. Let us not forget that these words were written thousands of years before the telescope was dreamed of.

The thesis of Moses in this paragraph, then, may be stated in these simple but profound words:

The solar and astronomical bodies are the result of special creation. This fact is established by three lines of thought:

It is stated by Scripture.

It is required by reason.

It is sustained by science.

On these three unanswerable arguments the fact is clearly and unqualifiedly demonstrated.

For the statements of Scripture we will content ourselves with a few out of the many that might be advanced. The first and the best known is, of course, the nineteenth Psalm:

"The heavens declare the glory of God, and the firmament showeth His handiwork. Day unto day uttereth speech, and night unto night showeth knowledge. There is no speech nor language where their voice is not heard. Their line is gone out through all the earth, and their words to the end of the world."

In this magnificent poem, the writer of the Divine Word states what the sages of all times have been quick to attest; that the heavens are their own best proof of special creation. There is no land so mean, no people so low, and no tongue so wanting in expression, that it has failed to testify that the psalmist was right. From one end of the earth to the other, the entire world has witnessed to these facts here so magnificently recorded in the living Word of the living God.

Again we note the record in the one hundred and second Psalm, the twenty-fifth verse: *"The heavens are the work of Thy hands."* Literally, this is true. The entire record of the Holy Bible sustains this statement. So we see the poetic prophet, Isaiah, crying out concerning His God: "He stretcheth out the heavens as a curtain, and spreadeth them out as a tent to dwell in . . ." Even the mournful prophet, Jeremiah, weeping over the sins of his people, ceases from his lamentations long enough to exclaim of the God of Israel, "Thus saith Jehovah, Who made the sun for a light by day, and the ordinances of the moon and of the stars for a light by night . . ." Who can gainsay the statement of the prophet here, that the stars follow known and established laws? "Ordinances," indeed, are the testimony of the stellar bodies; they obey the Divine Lawgiver all through the ages. Never do the stars rebel or seek to violate the laws which govern their activity; they seem to know their Creator and are content to obey Him.

This is the unvarying statement of the sacred Book, coinciding at all points with the contention of Moses, that the heavenly bodies are the result of special creation. This fact is stated by the Scripture.

It is required by reason as well. If the heavenly bodies were not created specifically, where did they come from? The thoughtless infidel may reply that they are the result of gases condensing, but he does not in any wise solve the difficulty. Where did the gases come from? There must be a beginning for all matter, and the stars and planets are certainly concrete substances. Their very elements are known to the student of astronomy, and their size, mass, bulk, gravity, and speed of rotation are also known in many cases. There they are, an eternal challenge to any intellect which dares face the issue; where did they come from? *Reason* demands a Creator.

The scientific standing of the late Lord Kelvin certainly can not be questioned now. He spent his life in studying the mysteries and laws of these sidereal bodies, and summed his entire philosophy up in one magnificent sentence: "Truly, the undevout astronomer would be mad!" He would indeed be. Either he would have to be mentally deficient, in order to note the law-abiding progress, the amazing number and stupendous size of these great worlds and systems and fail to appreciate the fact of God behind it all. Or else he would *go* mad trying to reason out a more acceptable theory to account for them. Reason requires specific creation.

This is required by reason because the mathematics of astronomical bodies are absolute. The science of numbers demands a mathematician, and back of the perfection of stellar mathematics there must be the Mind which solved these problems, established the ratios, and co-ordinated the factors of heavenly motion. There are scarcely a score of human intelligences alive today who can comprehend a tithe of the mathematics of space; how great, then, must have been the Intelligence which conceived and executed it all!

Creation of the heavenly orbs is required by reason because their laws are established. The law of man is in process of construction and change; scarcely a meeting of the legislature of any land ever passes without revision of existing law, and addition of new statutes. By experiment and experience we discover those laws that will avail and those that will not, but because we are a reasoning race we persevere until we have a comparatively able code.

Not so, however, in the realms of the heavenly spaces. Here the laws are *established*, and the mightiest star must obey them. They are never rescinded or amended, and no new ones are necessary after all these passing ages. Henry Drummond stated that there was natural law in the spiritual world; but certainly there is spiritual law in the natural world! For nothing short of spiritual law could have operated for the uncountable ages, and functioned forever without a break. So reason demands creation and a specific Creator.

The requirement of reason is in this case, as in all others.

sustained by science. If the mathematics of astronomy are absolute, it necessarily follows that scientific proof is therein contained, for the science of mathematics is the most rigid science of all. It is beyond the possibility of the scope of a single chapter in any book to attempt an exhaustive inquiry into the proofs and truths of astronomy, but we will introduce sufficient evidence at least to demonstrate the statement we have made. Science does sustain the contention of Moses in the fact of special creation to account for the skies and their contents. To the reader who desires a more extensive study, we can suggest the recent book by the able Sir James Jeans, "The Universe Around Us." That will give to any man, scientist or layman, food for thought for many days to come.

This is confessedly a difficult subject with which to deal. If the writer waxes technical, as many are tempted to do, the average reader is at once beyond his depth and quits in disgust. If the technical facts and language of astronomy are omitted, the author always feels that he has not done justice to his subject. But the universe is so immense and the mind of man is so restricted, our imagination reels before the contemplation of the entire galaxy above. In popular lectures on the subject of astronomy it is customary for the speaker to yield to the natural temptation of bewildering and dazzling his hearers by a trip into the immensity of the sidereal gigantia. He loses them somewhere along the pathway of light years! But since the purpose of this chapter is not to show the erudition of the author, but is rather to produce simple facts in defense of a thesis, we will avoid the discussion of sidereal facts that would bewilder more than illumine. So in order that we may avoid this confusion, and deal with factors that we can comprehend, we will begin with the solar system of which our planet, Earth, is a minor part; and a very minor part at that!

The first thing that strikes the new explorer in the realm of astronomy is the vast and inconceivable distances. So tremendous is the span of space comprehended in the sidereal heavens, that the mental traveler in this sphere has had to invent a new yardstick, or measure, called a light year. We know that light travels at the speed of one hundred eighty-six thousand two hundred miles a second. This distance, then, is a light second. A light minute would be sixty times a light second, or the distance light would travel in one minute. A light year is the distance a ray of light would travel at this speed in one solar year. We can express it in terms of millions of miles, but the mind does not really take it in.

We have also the astronomical unit, which is the distance of the earth from the sun. Since the orbit of the earth is elliptical, it follows that our unit must be the *mean* distance, which is ninety million miles. Here, then, is a unit that we can more nearly conceive, ninety millions of miles. How vast this is, we see when we note that the earth is only twenty-five thousand miles in circumference at the equator! The distance from the earth to the sun is thus seen to be three thousand, six hundred times the distance around the earth. This seems stupendous to us at first thought, but we next contemplate the fact that some of the planets in our system are as far away as thirty and more of these units from the sun. The planet Neptune, for instance, is some two billion, seven hundred ninety-three million, four hundred eighty-seven thousand miles from the sun. Even these vast distances sink into insignificance when we consider sidereal space in comparison with solar space. But it is not our purpose to bore the reader with distances and figures.

The next fact that impresses us is the thought of the immensity of some of these individual bodies that make up the system. The size of the planet Earth we fairly well comprehend; how vast then is the planet Jupiter, which is over thirteen hundred times as big as our earth! Contemplate this: if we wished to break up Jupiter into a string of beads, and make each bead as big as this earth, we would have a necklace of one thousand three hundred and twenty beads! Let us glance at some other facts of this system, and see how creation has operated to prepare a habitation for the race that is called Man.

The sun, of course, being the nucleus of this system, without which none of the rest of the system would be possible, is the most important. Its size is stupendous. It has a diameter of eight hundred sixty-four thousand miles, as compared with the eight thousand miles which is the diameter of the earth. The mass of the sun is three hundred and thirty thousand times the mass of the earth, and its volume is a million three hundred thousand times ours. Consider what this means: the planet Earth, on which we live, weighs six thousand nine hundred fifty-two quintillion (6,952,000,000,000,000,000, 000,000) tons. The sun weighs one million three hundred thousand times that much! Reason staggers and refuses to accept such a figure, and we need a more acceptable basis of comparison. To group this figure more clearly, note that we write the figures, 6,952, and follow that with twenty-one ciphers!

Again we find the simplest basis of comparison is the known and familiar facts concerning our own planet. The planet Earth has but the one moon, a beautiful satellite that rotates around our earth at the approximate mean distance of two hundred and forty thousand miles from us. In order to show the size of the sun, let us suppose that some superhuman workman with a stupendous machine hollowed out the sun, leaving a crust approximately one hundred thousand miles thick. The hollowed space within this sun would then accomodate the earth in the center. The moon could then revolve around the earth on its present orbit of a mean distance of two hundred and forty thousand miles, and still leave one hundred thousand miles of space between the outside of the revolving moon and the inside of the crust of the hollowed sun!

Squeeze all the planets and asteroids that are satellites of the sun into one vast body, and the sun is still five hundred times bigger than all these planets put together. Try to comprehend this: the mass of the planet Earth is two hundred sixty billion cubic miles, and the mass of the sun is three hundred and thirty times as large! Truly, the mind of man cannot take it in.

The sun is rapidly shrinking in size. Every second it evacuates into space four million seven hundred thousand tons of its matter in the form of solar energy. Thus it is contracting at the rate of about two hundred and fifty cubic feet a year. This is no cause for alarm, however, as this present rate of shrinking would cause the sun to lose one cubic mile of its mass in every six hundred million years. It is good for quite some time yet. We are reminded here of the Irishman who was attending a lecture on astronomy. The astronomer sought to impress his hearers with the rate of the sun's discharge of its inherent elements, and he said, "My friends, in about ten billion years the sun will probably be cold and dead like the moon, and all life will have perished from the planet."

In great excitement the Irishman called out, "How long did you say?"

The professor said, "About ten billion years."

"Thank God," the Irishman cried, "I thought you said ten *million*."

But as far as we are concerned, personally, ten million more years of sunshine is just as good as ten billion!

The temperature of the sun, at the surface of the orb, is about ten thousand degrees Fahrenheit. Imagine that, in the light of the hot weather of Earth's summers, when we suffer at ninety-eight degrees! The sun also turns on its axis at such a speed it completes a diurnal revolution in about twenty-nine days.

We are not to suppose, however, that this body called the sun, is large in the roll call of heavenly orbs. Indeed, it is probably one of the smallest suns known, and we, one of the most insignificant solar systems in existence! The sun Vega, for instance, that is visible in our summer sky, has a diameter thirty-eight times the diameter of the sun, being thirty-three million, five hundred seventy-six thousand miles across. It has a volume fifty-five thousand times the volume of the sun.

Around our flaming sun, then, governed, controlled, and warmed by it, there are nine planets. *Only one of them is inhabited,* the planet Earth. Indeed, as Jeans demonstrates in his recent book, referred to above, this planet Earth, insignificant and tiny in the space of the heavens, is the only one that *could* support life. It is evident, then, that we were designed for this planet, and more important still, *this planet was designed for us!*

Now, that is just what Moses is contending for in the first chapter of Genesis. Before God created the human family, he prepared one, and only one, planet for the reception of the race. The record of that preparation is contained in the six days of the first chapter of Genesis, which we have under present consideration. We repeat, then, that this planet was prepared by Divine wisdom and power to receive the human race. Science sustains this contention, as we shall now see.

The planet Mercury could not support the human, vegetable or animal kingdoms. Nothing could live there. Mercury is only a bit less than thirty-six million miles from the sun, and it is a torrid planet indeed. It receives seven times our amount of light and heat from the sun, and could not possibly be conceived of as habitable. There is no atmosphere to breathe, and no moisture of any kind or amount on the planet. No rains, no streams, no lakes, no springs, no oceans, and no fogs.

At the temperature of seven hundred degrees in the summer time, no moisture could exist, and the blood would boil out of the human veins. The light would sear the eyeballs of any creature that had sight, and the furnace of the atmosphere

(if there were one) would scorch the lungs of any living creature. Even the fabled Phoenix could not live on Mercury!

What an amazing world it would be, then, if we could exist
on such a planet! For while its day is the same as ours, close
to twenty-four hours, Mercury is so close to the sun, and her
orbital speed is so great, that as a consequence her year is only
eighty-seven days, twenty-three hours and twenty-five minutes
long! Imagine living where there were only twenty-two days
to each of the four seasons! Small boys at least would be happy, where Christmas came every eighty-seven days.

At the opposite extreme is Uranus, the frozen planet. This
neighboring planet is so far away from the sun, it gets less
than one-hundredth the amount of light and heat that this
earth receives. Its orbit is so vast in spite of its speed, that one
year on Uranus would be equal to eighty-four of our years
here. Think of it, a man who was seventy-five years old on this
planet, if he were transported to Uranus would have to wait
nine years to have his first birthday up there. How could life
exist, where there was one harvest in every eighty-four years?
Groping about in the dark like moles; shivering in the frozen
atmosphere of three hundred degrees below zero, like Africans
suddenly transported to the North Pole! No air to breathe
and no water to drink; how bleak a prospect to contemplate!

This same reasoning applies to every other planet in the
solar system. Earth is the only possible place where life could
exist, and this is the one place God has placed us in which to
live. How truly Moses spoke, we see when we consider how we
fit this planet, and how this planet is fitted to us! Many lines
of thought will suggest themselves to the earnest thinker; we
can only pause to note a few.

The inclination of the earth on its axis, twenty-three and a
half degrees off the perpendicular, is an amazing provision
for human habitation on this globe. Man would not so design
his place of residence, as he has a passion for mathematical and
mechanical perfection, and everything he does and builds

must be "plumb." Yet this very departure from what we would nominally call perfection, provides for the seasons that make life so varied and joyful. This combines, of course, with the orbital rotation of the earth around the sun.

We note, however, that in mid-winter, when the year is the coldest, the earth is the closest to the sun! In the dead of winter we are three million miles nearer the sun than we are in the heat of the summer. But this tilting of the earth on its axis causes a certain deflection in the rays of the sun as they reach our atmosphere. Thus the day grows colder and shorter as the earth reaches the flat side of its ellipse, and we have the delightful seasons to enjoy.

Equally remarkable is God's provision in the diurnal revolution of the earth, that results in day and night. If the earth were stationary in space, what a dismal life ours would be! There would be no sunrises and no sunsets, no day and no night. If we happened to be born on the sunny side of the planet, we would never know the blessed relief that night brings to tired eyes after the glare of the day, unless we journeyed half way around the globe. We would never see a star or know that there was a moon, and the flaming glory of the galaxy would all be lost to us. What strange confusion this would result in, when the clocks ran down or needed adjusting! Without the daily check against the heavenly bodies we could not keep our clocks straight, and bedlam would result from living in eternal sunshine.

Worse still would be the lot of those who dwelt on the dark side of the planet in eternal night. Never a ray of sunshine would lighten their bleak existence, and they would have to grope in the dark or depend entirely upon artificial lights. Such vegetation as managed to survive would be the ghastly pale freaks that we now see growing in dark cellars, and if there were such things as flowers they would all be of a ghostly sameness. With no color or beauty, and utterly devoid of perfume, as these flowers would be, they would mature into a tragic parody of fruit, tasteless and without aroma.

It is difficult to realize just how much is embraced in this simple statement of Moses, that God, by this simple means, "divided the day from the night." We are so used to this provision of His grace that we are apt to forget how marvelous it is. So let us consider what we mean by the term day. The day, as here intended in the text, is a period of time consumed in the complete single rotation of the earth on its axis. Out in space the sun is shining without pause, its light ceaselessly pervading space. This planet being in the shape of a globe, it follows that the side of the sphere facing the sun will be bathed in the light of that orb, and the side of the globe that is away from the sun must be in the shadow of the planet itself. From the beginning it has been the custom to call the light half of the rotation day, and the dark half night. But the two halves of the cycle of rotation, day and night, are also jointly spoken of as one day. That is to say, then, a day is one complete revolution of the earth in the face of the sun. This motion is called the "diurnal" revolution, and we will continue to refer to it as such.

This motion is not absolute in its speed. That is to say, at different points in the orbit of the earth around the sun, the diurnal revolution is faster or slower than at other points. But for the sake of convenience we strike an average, and the civil day of twenty-four hours is a mean of all the solar days in one year. We say twenty-four hours, but that is not exactly correct. The mean day is really twenty-three hours, fifty-six minutes, four and nine one-hundredths seconds. Thus God has established the period of rotation, and the earth must keep this speed and this schedule.

Lest the reader might think it is unnecessary to be so particular about the nine one-hundredths of a second in the day, let us note here that creation takes into account the most insignificant details. We do not know how long the earth has thus been revolving in its diurnal motion, but let us suppose it has been ten thousand years. Now if the earth had lost one-hundredth of a second each revolution, that is, if the fraction of a second we deal with, were eight one-hundredths of a second instead of nine, at the end of these ten thousand years the day would now be only eighteen hours long, and the year but two hundred and twenty-nine days.

The entire cycle of organic life has been set to meet this exact cycle. Twelve hours of light for labor, and twelve hours of dark for rest. The plants and the animals demand this, and they suffer if this program is interfered with. We have observed plants under the influence of artificial light with no rest periods of darkness, and their life cycle is shortened, their fruit is aborted, and their entire purpose of being is thwarted, because they were created to fit this cycle of twenty-four hours.

Man, by the exercise of his ingenuity, may change the order of his living, but all who have tried it testify to the unnatural manner of life when this habit is disarranged. Workers in the darkness hours have repeatedly complained that their life was extremely drab and uninteresting, and very few men choose the "night shift" by preference. So the fact that we are designed to fit this peculiar "day" that governs our living is an evidence that we were planned by Intelligence for this one planet, on which alone life is found.

In the same manner, we find that the second motion of the planet on which we live, is planned to meet the needs of our life as well. This motion is the orbital revolution, or the journey of the earth around the sun. It takes three hundred and sixty-five days, five hours, forty-eight minutes and forty-nine seconds for this cycle to be completed, and when the earth has made this one circle we call it a year. This journey is not made in an exact circle, but is on an ellipse, which we might define somewhat crudely by calling it egg-shaped. This is highly important to the life on this planet, and must not be disregarded as an evidence of creation.

The speed of this planet on this annual journey is tremendous. We think we have achieved something remarkable in the air-craft that will fly two hundred and fifty miles an hour, but this steady old earth is journeying through space at the rate of seventy-two thousand, six hundred miles an hour! We boast of two miles a minute in the automobile, but at the same time we fail to remember that we are riding through space on our planetary chariot at the speed of a thousand one hundred and ten miles every minute! Reduce that to the speed of eighteen and a half miles in one second, and you will see that we are really traveling! Pick out in your mind some nearby city, that you can reach in your car in half an hour by fast driving. Now to get an idea of speed, note that the earth travels that far while your watch ticks one second.

No other planet in space has this same annual period. We are the only planet in any known system with this exact rate of travel. This is important to note, as this factor helps to make our four seasons and determine their length. On Jupiter, for instance, the year is twelve times the length of ours. A sixty year old man leaving the earth to migrate to Jupiter, would find himself but five years old when he arrived. It would be a weird place on which to live, with a day of less than ten hours, and each of the four seasons three years long. On Saturn the year is thirty times the length of our year, and on far-away Neptune it takes a hundred and sixty-four of our years to equal one on that planet.

The only "speed cops" in space seem to be those that keep the speeders moving at their allotted pace. No force or power stops the speeding planets for red lights and traffic jams. Real intelligence has provided for all that from the beginning. The earth must maintain her speed! If this hastening planet had lost just two seconds for every million miles she has traveled in the brief period of written human history, the month of September would have become instead the month of April! It is essential that no time be lost.

The factor of error in human achievement of perfection of schedule is gross compared to this amazing record! If a railroad system could boast that it had not lost two seconds from its schedule in a million miles traveled, it would advertise this that all the world might marvel. Yet the earth maintains this rigid adherence to the time-table of God, and all as a matter of course. Truly His hand is on His creation, and all created things give evidence of His power and might.

The cycle of life on this planet is set to *this* clock as well as to that of the diurnal revolution. It takes just the four seasons to produce the vegetation, without which life on this globe would be impossible; and it must not vary through the ages. The spring for the time of planting, the summer to grow, the fall to mature, ripen, and reap, and the winter to rest the soil and the planter as well. Yes, even the ground has to rest and recuperate, as every farmer can testify. The elements abstracted from the soil must be replaced, and this replacement must be by the natural means of the winter weather, or by the artificial means of chemical fertilizer. In the wilderness where there is no man, but where the creatures of the wild depend on growing things to sustain their life, having no chemical fertilizers, they must depend upon the winter for this ministry of rehabilitation.

In certain zones where the climate is mild and does not divide itself into four distinct seasons, the ground may be utilized every month in the year, provided certain artificial aids are given. In some cases this aid comes from scientific planting and crop rotation. Again, it is necessary under other circumstances to spread multiplied tons of chemical salts upon the surface, in order to replenish the elements that have been depleted from the soil. Occasionally this is accomplished by the use of such cover crops as vetch and nitrogenous producing vegetation. In the wilderness, of course, where the cycle of nature is not interfered with by the commercial interests of mankind, all this replenishment is cared for by the natural mechanism that is understood by all who are familiar with the tropic regions. Over a vast portion of the earth's surface, however, the necessary replenishment of the soil is cared for by the recuperation of winter.

Who can truly study this line of evidences and fail to see that all this mass of facts testifies with unerring power to the truth of the Mosaic contention, namely, that it all results from the specific act of a personal Creator? Only those of whom the Scriptures say, "The god of this world hath blinded their hearts, that they might believe a lie," can reject the testimony of the works of God to the truth of His Word.

Let us also note the fact of our fortunate distance from the sun, as a further evidence of design in the arrangement of this globe for human habitation. Thousands of mathematically possible orbits for this planet may be planned, but only the present orbit would suffice for life as it is seen here. What fortunate chance (?) arranged our distance from the sun to the exact factor necessary to make the earth habitable? If we had the orbit of Mercury the life of this globe would burn up; in the orbit of Saturn, Jupiter, Neptune, or Uranus, life would perish by freezing. Here we are, then, by Providence placed just close enough to the sun to live, and just far enough away so that we perish not. To the mind that cannot see design and intelligence in this blessed arrangement, the light of reason is a stranger, and facts make no appeal. But to the person of intelligence, these truths must make the same strong case for creation that the wisest of earth's thinkers have always recognized. Science sustains the demand of reason for a specific creation and a Creator.

This is seen again when we note the factor of gravity on this our habitation. Beyond argument, man is destined to endure just the gravity factor we meet on this planet. On the planet Mercury, for instance, the factor of gravity is to our gravity as two is to five. That is to say, an object that weighs five pounds on this earth, would weigh only two pounds on Mercury. Imagine a man who weighed a hundred and fifty pounds leaving this earth, and landing on that neighbor planet. When he arrived he would weigh just sixty pounds. If he took an ordinary step, such as he was accustomed to take in walking at home, he would land ten feet away. If he jumped for a window ledge or rafter, he would spring up in the air a distance of thirty feet! Life would be utterly inconceivable in such a situation.

No less awkward would be the case of a man from the earth who was in some manner transported to the planet Jupiter. Using our factor of gravity as a unit, we find that the gravity of Jupiter is two point sixty-six. That means that an object that on earth weighs a hundred and fifty pounds, would weigh on Jupiter three hundred and ninety-nine pounds. A man weighing a hundred and fifty pounds, if he sought to walk in the gravity of Jupiter, would crawl along as though he bore on his back a burden of two hundred and forty-nine pounds. His legs would buckle and fail, and his very bones would groan with the unbearable burden of his own weight.

Is it accident, then, which has so marvelously fitted us for this sphere on which our lot is happily cast? Reason cannot accept so puerile an explanation; it demands an intelligent reply. The only one that science can offer in response to the demand of reason, is the age-old contention of Moses, that God created the planet for our habitation; created us to fit the prepared environment; and then gave us this record that we might know and believe. Science, then, sustains the demand of reason, and provides the physical facts to assure us of the truth of the writings of Moses.

We must not consider that we have exhausted the subject with this brief review of some of the facts of this solar system. Such is indeed far from the case. We have yet to consider the fact of the stars that are far and away above and beyond our solar system, and even past and outside our galaxy. For this solar system that we inhabit is but a tiny one in a cluster of

millions of such systems, and there are other galaxies of systems far larger than our entire company of systems. The mind
reels in the contemplation of their number and their size and
grandeur; but there they shine as an eternal testimony to the
truth of this chapter of Genesis. And beyond those galaxies
that are visible to the eye of man, like silver snails in the garden of God, shine the great spiral nebulae, each of them a universe as vast in extent as the one of which we form a humble
and insignificant part.

We merely mention them because they are truly part of the
work of the Fourth Day, when the mists were rolled away in
obedience to the spoken word of God, and their splendor was
made visible to the face of this earth. From that hour to this,
they have never ceased to shine down their message of the God
who made and established them, nor ceased from obeying His
laws and His ordinances. To this very day they show the
glory of God, and speak of His handiwork.

There is, of course, a spiritual significance to all of this
physical fact, as is always the case in the Bible. Every creature
and phase of creation in some manner typifies the work of God
in redemption, and prophesies of that glad release from bondage that shall some day gladden the entire creation.

So we see, then, that in the Old Testament as well as in the
New, the glorious sun that lights our day is set as a picture of
the Lord Jesus Christ, who is the Son of God. This fact is evidenced clearly by the prophet Malachi, who writes:

"But unto you that fear my name shall the Sun of Righteousness arise with healing in His wings, and ye shall go
forth and gambol as calves of the stall."

This promise of joy and happiness, healing and assuaging
of sorrow and misery, is made by God's prophet to God's people, Israel, and will be fulfilled when Jesus shall come again.
Seeking, then, for a term of grandeur and splendor to portray
His adored Person, the prophet takes the flaming orb of day
as the only fitting symbol.

Isaiah also applies this figure to the person of the Lord Jesus. The sixtieth chapter of Isaiah contains some of the grandest poetry that was ever written in any tongue. The song of Israel's redemption and triumph in this chapter reaches its climax in these beautiful words:

> "The sun shall be no more thy light by day, neither for brightness shall the moon give light unto thee, but the Lord shall be unto thee an everlasting light, and thy God shall be thy glory. Thy sun shall no more go down, neither shall thy moon withdraw itself, for the Lord shall be thine everlasting light, and the days of thy mourning shall be ended."

In these exquisite words of wondrous promise, the beautiful future of Israel is portrayed. In language surpassing mere human vocabulary, the Lord, who is Jesus the Christ, is portrayed as the sun and the light of His people, and the everlasting light of His radiance is to shine upon the path of the nation, when they turn to Christ at His unveiling.

In the same manner the New Testament writers portray the Lord Jesus in His resurrection splendor and grace. John, in his Patmos vision, sees the exalted Saviour, and in his description John says:

> ". . . and He had in His right hand seven stars, and out of His mouth proceeded a sharp two-edged sword, *and His countenance was as the sun shineth in His strength.*"

This thought is continued in John's description of the New Jerusalem, as in the twenty-first chapter, where the revelator says:

> "And the city hath no need of the sun, neither of the moon, to shine upon it, for the glory of God did lighten it, and the Lamb is the light thereof."

And once more in the next chapter the text continues to paint the splendor and beauty of the Saviour under this figure in these words:

"And there shall be night no more; and they need no light of lamp, neither light of sun. *For the Lord God shall be light,* and they shall reign for ever and ever."

This characterization of the Lord Jesus, whose glory is as the brightness of the sun that shines in the full strength of his noonday power, is again shown in the vision that Paul had of the Lord Jesus, when the chosen apostle saw the ascended Saviour on the road to Damascus. There can be no question that Paul actually saw the Lord, as his entire transformed life thereafter is an indisputable evidence of that fact. From that day on, he who had been the fiercest enemy of the Christian faith became its boldest champion. Paul himself accounts for this change by the fact that he saw the Lord.

Now when this incident occurred, the glory of the brightness of the person of Jesus, who then, as now, graced the right hand of the Majestic Glory on high, caused Saul to fall to the earth, blinded by the brightness of the person of Christ. With a brightness stronger than the fiercest rays of the summer sun, the sight of Saul was seared, and as he fell on his face in pain, he could only cry out in wonder, "Who art thou, Lord?" Back came the answer from the bright and flaming One, "I am Jesus, Whom thou persecutest." The Scriptures abound with such illustrations. Jesus is the Sun of Righteousness.

By analogy, then, the moon is the church. The moon would never be visible if it were not for the power and presence of the sun, and in like manner none would have ever known of the institution which is the church, if the Lord Jesus, the Sun of Righteousness, had not graced the earth with His presence. Also, we note that when the sun arises the moon goes into obscurity, and in like fashion the Scriptures reveal that when the Saviour returns the institution of the church will pass away. In that day no man will *need* to say, "Teach me of the Lord" (which is the function of the church) but all shall know Him, from the least to the greatest. In the day when the earth is filled with the knowledge of the love of God as the waters cover the sea, the service of the church will have been fulfilled, and the moon will have set.

Again, we see that the moon has neither life nor light of her own, but shines only by reflecting the glory of the sun. She is a cold, dead, and barren planet in her own self, but when she turns her face toward the living sun she glows with a light that is majestic. Her function is to relieve the gross darkness in the absence of the sun and so we note that while the Lord Jesus is away, and until the time of His return, the church is to shine forth the reflected light of the glory of Christ. In this way her task is to lighten the night of sin and the black horror of iniquity, and only that church is a real church that truly reflects the Lord Jesus Christ to a lost and darkened world. The church that has not Christ has no light, and where there is no light, there is no life as well.

Beyond question, in this allegory, and in the type of the sacred Scripture, the stars are the individual believers in Jesus Christ, commonly called Christians. Daniel tells us this in the twelfth chapter of his prophecy, with these words: "They that turn many to righteousness shall shine as the stars for ever and ever." Who are they that turn many to righteousness? They are the individual Christians who live their faith, and who testify to the transforming power of the redeeming Christ. No man can be turned to righteousness by any other means than this; he must be brought into allegiance and surrender to Jesus Christ. Then having found this great salvation, it is inevitable that he will seek to turn others to the joy and the righteousness that he has found, and thus he shines as the stars, for ever and ever.

The New Testament makes the same bold claim, that the individual who is born again by the power of the Holy Spirit, is the perfect fulfillment of the type intended by the stars. In the Philippian Epistle, the second chapter, Paul, writing under the power and inspiration of the Holy Spirit, appeals to the Christian in these magnificent words:

"Do all things without murmurings and disputings, that ye may become blameless and harmless, children of God, without blemish in the midst of a crooked and darkened generation, *among whom ye shine as lights in the world.*"

This word here translated "lights" is the Greek word "phoster," and it means luminary, light container, or simply star. The Christian, then, is to shine in this present world as a star.

To what purpose is this beautiful figure given? Let us recall that Moses said of the stars that they were for *signs* and for *seasons*, etc. Many a weary wanderer, lost in the blackness of a darkened night, has thanked God when the storm was lifted, so that he might see the stars, and find his way back home to safety and to peace. The stars are for signs, and that tells the whole tale of God's expectation of us.

It is the business of the "stars" to lead men to Christ. Do you remember that when the Wise Men found the Saviour, they had followed the star? Our task then is to shine out and on; *the wise will follow this shining and find God.* In contrast to all this, how pitiful is the man who is described by Jude in his scathing words addressed to the false teacher and the Christless preacher, when he tells them they are "wild waves of the sea, foaming out their own shame, *wandering stars,* for whom the blackness of darkness hath been reserved forever." Let us praise God that He hath committed to men, the Light that is Christ, and may that Light so shine from us, the luminaries, that many may, through our shining, be prepared to receive the Sun of Righteousness with joy when He shall arise with healing in His wings.

The Rapidly Multiplying Creatures

Genesis Chapter One:

20. And God said, Let the waters bring forth abundantly the moving creature that hath life, and fowl *that* may fly about the earth in the open firmament of heaven.

21. And God created great whales, and every living creature that moveth, which the waters brought forth abundantly, after their kind, and every winged fowl after his kind: and God saw that *it was* good.

22. And God blessed them, saying, Be fruitful, and multiply, and fill the waters in the seas, and let fowl multiply in the earth.

23. And the evening and the morning were the fifth day.

CHAPTER EIGHT

The Rapidly Multiplying Creatures

IN THE paragraph from Genesis which the reader has just perused on the opposite page, there is exhibited a revelation that is stupendous in its superhuman recitation of tremendous events. Can we imagine any purely human authority penning a paragraph that in the brief limits of ninety-three *words* tells the student all that many volumes of biology and zoology attempt to convey? The wisdom of man is not manifested in simple terms, and the very brevity of this amazing section of the Revelation marks it as of Divine origin. The account is so clear and precise that in the English Bible, not one word has to be interpolated by the translators to clear up the meaning of the text.

We have never read a book that satisfactorily explained the mystery of the *origin* of life; except the books that agree with these words from the pen of Moses. The theory of evolution offers no explanation of how life began, but begins with life already here, and seeks to show how it changed from simple forms into higher orders. The various texts of biology and zoology, philosophy and botany, that deal with this question either evade the issue entirely, or confess their ignorance, or agree with the record of the first chapter of Genesis. It is this record that God gave to Moses, the account of the events of the fifth day in the week of creation that will occupy our attention in this and the following chapter.

This day marks the second appearance in the first chapter of Genesis of the word "bara," which is "to create." In many ways it is the most intriguing of the six days, as there was more variety of accomplishment on this day than on any other. In this one brief span of time, the Creator originates, and places in motion and vital functioning, all the many varieties that dwell in the water, the entire realm of bird life, and the insect world as well. When we consider the amazing numbers of these orders, the significance of this day grows even beyond the limits of the word phenomenal! Thousands upon thousands of orders, families, genera, species, and varieties fill the water and the air, and all are comprehended in the boundless expanse of the work of God on this one day.

It is in connection with this appearance of biological life, quite naturally, that the word "bara" again makes its appearance. This is the initial appearance of this word in the text as touching the work of the six days; as the first appearance of the creation-word is in the first verse, and refers to events that were consummated ages before this week of creation began. The other words that have been used to define the type of work of each day have all been considered in their place, so we will merely remark here that vegetation was the only kind of life existing when this fifth day dawned. It is apparent to even the casual observer that the plants *must* precede the animal creation, or there will be no source of food for the latter. Similarly, when the birds are this day created, they appear after the insects, or contemporarily with them. Thus the seed and edible part of the vegetation have a start on the creatures that are to consume them. We have no doubt that the God who could make Aaron's rod bud, blossom, and bear fruit in the space of twelve hours, had been able to arrange sufficient food for all the creatures that were later to demand that sustenance.

In speaking of the vegetation, the sacred record states that God's command was couched in the phraseology which meant release from restraint. He is there recorded as saying, "Let the grass *spring up*." It has been suggested by many commentators on this passage, that the seeds of the vegetation may have been lying dormant in the wreck of the previous order awaiting the end of chaos so that they might thrust themselves forth again. Without any attempt to settle that question, we content ourselves with noting that the account does say the grass and the vegetation kingdom were all to "spring up" on that third day.

Here, however, no such possibility could be considered. If the preceding age, antedating the period of chaos, *did* have life in a sentient form, all of it would have perished in the catastrophe that wrecked that order, and no semblance of it could have survived the ice age of which Moses speaks. So that any life of the higher types, commonly called biological, to distinguish it from the botanical, would have to be produced by specific and fiat creation at that particular moment.

Of course, no man can say that there was, or was not, life in that preceding age, but it is interesting to speculate on the possibility, and to note that there may be a basis here for the contention of those who hold that the fossil creatures are there and thus accounted for. Any living forms that may have perished in the upheaval following the first verse of Genesis, and left their bodies or bones to rest in the wreck during the chaotic age, would certainly have been thoroughly fossilized by the time man began to dig them up! But as we are not interested in speculation now, but rather in the pure facts of science that can be made to shed light upon this sacred page, let us proceed to an examination of the words of Moses, and see how accurate they are.

Let us note first of all, that Moses contends that the seat of life, or at least the sphere of its first and lowest appearance, is in the water. How can we account for this strange anticipation of the modern school of zoology and its contentions, on any other basis than that of revelation? Every text book, and every teacher who deals with the science of life, will agree with Moses, and say that the lowest forms of life known are water dwellers, and that the water was undoubtedly the first realm to harbor and support life. Indeed, it is this present agreement with the Divine record that gives the evolutionary school the single semblance of logic it possesses. This school also confesses the truth of Moses' statement here, and from this basis of fact, that water is the seat of the lowest forms of life at present known, they proceed to draw their unwarranted conclusions as to the origin, from these low forms, of all the higher kinds. There is a gulf between the land dwellers and the water denizens that has never been bridged, and never will be. We state that with such confidence because we know that even science cannot by research establish that which never was, and since the higher forms most decidedly *did not* evolve from the lower, no bridge can span the gap that is as wide as eternity.

Certain textual notes are necessary at the start of this study, as these words are of special significance in the light of present day scientific truth. In the phrasing of the text there is a slight difference between the King James Version and the American Revised Version of the English Bible, and we will note this as well. The King James Version reads: "Let the waters bring forth abundantly the moving creature that hath life . . ." and it may seem to suggest that the water produced or generated this life. The text is clearer in the Revised Version, and closer to the Hebrew, which makes no suggestion that the water may have caused or produced the life. This text reads, "Let the waters *swarm with swarms* of living creatures . . ."

To clear up this passage, let us contrast three Hebrew words that appear in the text of this first chapter of Genesis. The first of these is in the eleventh verse, where the writer says, "Let the earth put forth grass . . ." This word "put forth" is the Hebrew "dasha," and it means "to spring up." It is used only three times in the entire Old Testament, and has this specific meaning in each case.

The second word is in the twenty-fourth verse, where the text has this: ". . . let the earth bring forth cattle . . ." Here we have the Hebrew word "jatsa" which is ever and only used of animal life. It means issue by genealogy and is reserved for the higher orders of life.

The third word appearing in this verse under consideration, is the word "sharats," which means literally "to swarm with myriads." This is the term Moses used to define the work of this day, when God says, "Let the water swarm with swarms of living creatures."

The twenty-first verse also attracts our attention with this phrase: "Every living creature that moveth." This is in Hebrew, literally, "the rapidly multiplying creatures." In all the literature of the world, this is the most marvelously concise and conclusive description of the creatures that dwell in an aqueous environment! There is no exception to this; the creatures which inhabit the waters are the most rapid multipliers in the world, as we shall see in a later section of this study. Moses again scores on the basis of modern scientific knowledge; he seemed to know biology and protozoology before these sciences were dreamed of, or else he spoke by inspiration, and divine knowledge was manifested through him!

The word he uses for water, the Hebrew term "yam," is applicable to an ocean, a lake, a sea, or a pond; rivers, springs, brooks, and pools are all permissible within the scope of this word, and the water dwellers are all grouped by the nature of their dwelling.

How literally do these creatures strive to obey the command of their Creator! In the twenty-second verse the record is inscribed, "Be fruitful, and multiply, and fill the waters . . ." and these orders never slack their diligence or halt their obedience to these words. The fecundity of the water dwellers is one of the amazing points of interest to all who study them. How slow seems the rate of reproduction of the mammals, for instance, in comparison with that of the fishes.

A female mackerel lays about five hundred thousand eggs at a time. How profitable it would be to the farmer who could cross a mackerel with a Plymouth Rock, and get a hen which would do half that well! So if we start with just one pair of mackerel, and all their progeny escape the dangers of sea life

and come to maturity, while they in turn each raise their entire family, the mackerel would in ten years fill all the oceans
on the face of the globe. The ocean is deep as well as wide,
parts of the Pacific being over thirty-two thousand feet in
depth. This is a bit more than six miles deep! Yet in ten years
the progeny of one pair of mackerel would fill all the oceans
so full that we could walk from continent to continent, and
from island to island, dry shod, on the backs of living mackerel!

The herring are even more literal in their obedience to the
divine order, and their fecundity is even more startling. If the
progeny of one pair of herring were unchecked for twenty
years, in that time they would equal the bulk of the entire
globe. Write down the figures 338, follow that with fifteen
ciphers, and that would be the number of tons the progeny of
one herring would weigh in twenty years, if they all came to
maturity! How the creatures of the modern world continue to
obey the injunction of God as recorded in the words of Moses!
and how true to modern knowledge his record is!

*The subject under discussion, that of modern science and
the creative days,* implies that there is harmony between this
record of old, and our modern scientific research knowledge.
The student will begin to raise objections to this and we cannot meet those objections by mere reiteration of the statement
of the case, but we must produce the evidence. Fortunately,
we are able so to do. Moses here states the fact of specific creation, and the question will at once be raised. "Is this in harmony with the science of the present day?"

In answer, let us first note that modern science has no reply
to make to the problem of origins. That is confessedly outside
of the field of scientific endeavor, which can deal only with
things *as they are.* Even the theory of evolution, which so
many men of science accept, has no explanation of the *origin*
of life. This school of speculation begins with life *here* and
proceeds to build on that fact a chain of improbabilities that

research has recently exploded. Now, even if the writing of Moses were to be accepted only as a working hypothesis, this Genesis account would at least have the backing of every fact that is known to science, for there is not a true biological discovery that ever has been made which does not confirm the theory of specific creation. At least we can say in support of Moses that there is nothing alive, or that ever has been alive, that could not have been specially created just that way. On the other side of the question, the world of biology, paleontology, and zoology teems with myriads of forms that cannot be reconciled with the evolutionary theory. So that, even if we view the first chapter of Genesis as a theory only, it is at least a reasonable theory and may be scientifically adopted as a working hypothesis. On the other hand, the alternate theory, that of evolution, is utterly discredited scientifically.

We do not advance the first chapter of Genesis as a theory, however, but boldly contend that it is a scientific record of absolute facts. We dare not make so bold a statement unless we can produce the evidence to sustain it, and we hasten to that agreeable and simple task.

The reader has, of course, noted in these studies, that all the *elements* of life are already in existence before this fifth day dawns. They have been associating in the soil, in the sea, and in the atmosphere as well. So far, life has not been evoked by a natural, unaided combination of elements, as the materialist, who rejects the creation theory, must contend. Since this naturalistic school of thought also insists that these days of creation were ages long, they have had ample time now in the preceding four periods for life to emerge by spontaneous generation, if ever it was going to do so. This last slim hope of the infidel is now recognized by true science as an impossibility; there is no evidence that spontaneous generation of life ever occurred, or indeed ever could have occurred. The entire body of laboratory *knowledge* is dead set against the theory, and none but the wildest dreamers hold the idea today.

We wish it *could* be accomplished in some modern series of experiments; for then Moses would be vindicated with a vengeance! The Mosaic contention is simply this: *"Life did not appear until called forth by supreme intelligence.* And the reason that it cannot be done today is because man is not intelligent enough to do it! But when a super-intellect emerges from the ruck of human kind (if he ever does) and at last succeeds in organizing life in the test tube, he will have demonstrated what Moses contends, that life came only when superior intelligence caused it to be. That man is not known yet, in spite of the wisdom of which we boast, nor is science looking for him in the near future!

No human power has as yet accomplished this amazing work. The last attempt that was hailed by the press as a success, was the attempt of a young Russian biologist. He succeeded in producing, or rather, organizing, five low forms of life in his test tube. The fact that they were of the lowest forms known did not militate against the wonders of his accomplishment, as that is just what we would expect to get from inorganic substances. He arranged his chemicals in a certain order in the test tube, subjected them to considerable heat, and eight hours later he had infusoria living in the tube.

His announcement startled the world of biology, and as his formula was revealed, many other biologists tried to follow his experiments. But, alas, nobody except the discoverer seemed able to make it work. All that the others got was a mass of chemicals, no more alive than they had been when they reposed on the laboratory shelves. So they suggested that the discoverer repeat the experiments under observation so the rest could watch and see what mistakes they had made, if any. The young scientist suggested instead that they go through with the experiment while *he* watched *them,* and he could then correct any error they made. The last stage of the technique was to impregnate the mass with a gas (CO_2) before the mass was subjected to heat, and as the experimenters proceeded to do this, the inventor of the method said, "There is your trouble, gentlemen; you are using *chemical* carbon dioxide. You must use gas that has been generated *by rotting vegetation!*" That, of course, pricked the bubble; the balloon collapsed. Gas generated by rotting vegetation is simply teeming with the spores, or eggs, of a multitude of living creatures, and all this chap had done was to *incubate* them in his test tube. He had created life no more than the farmer does when he puts eggs in his incubator to hatch out by artificial heat!

So we see that the hope of the materialist is a vain one; and the question of the time factor in these "days" of Genesis does not even enter in here; long or short, solar or geological, none of them produced or supported *life* until it leaped into instant being in response to a Divine command. That is a simple statement to make, but a profound fact to contemplate. In response to the spoken Word of God, instantly and miraculously, life appears for the first time, to grace the planet; and instantly starts to do what it was created for; that is, to reproduce after its own kind. From this obedience and program it has never deviated in a single instance or individual all through the ages which have elapsed since the word was here spoken.

Moses, then, seems to be in harmony not only with the scientific demonstration of the *method* of life origination, to-wit, creation, but he also here displays a remarkable knowledge of two other basic laws of biology recognized by every modern scholar and authority in this field. The first of these is that life can come only *from* life and the other is that life can reproduce only the kind of life which it in turn inherited from its ancestors. Trace it back through all the past until the research is obscured by the swirling mists of antiquity, and it will be found that there is no exception to this law: life comes only from living ancestors. The other law is equally basic and established: when a living creature gives birth or rise to another living creature, it is always a *creature of the same kind.* There may be, and often are, variations of that kind, such as a difference in color, modified stature, or some such minor detail, but a dog remains a dog whether it is a fox terrier or a St. Bernard!

This record, then, introduces our problem: *In the face of the contentions of the philosophy of organic evolution, how can the statements of Moses be scientifically established?* The task is relatively simple, for the same evidences of biology which shattered the theory of evolution have substantiated, sustained and established the truth of the record of the first chapter of Genesis.

The first evidence, of course, is the evidence of design in the created things which are, and have been, alive. Intelligence cannot admit that marvelous and intricate design could have just happened; especially when that design is repeatedly multiplied millions of times! We might be justified in crying "coincidence" if there were just one living creature, or a few living ones which seemed to display a creative intelligence back of their origin; but coincidence cannot be stretched to include hundreds of orders, thousands of genera, millions of species, and billions of individuals! Every creature which lives in the sea, the air, or on the land, as well as every creature which ever did live, and which has left its fossil bones to tell the tale of the past, cries aloud the fact of design in its creation. Not one fact can be produced to refute this.

To show *how* the evidences of design are seen in the created things, we will begin with the smallest creatures Moses mentions on this fifth day, and ascend through the scale of creation to the largest. We noted in a paragraph above that Moses seemed to know a great deal about the protozoa, yet of course we recognize that as an impossibility. The minute creatures of the microscopic world were not visible to the eye of man until the microscope was invented, and Moses could not have known that a thousand tiny creatures could dwell in a drop of water, unless he had the aid of such a modern instrument! Yet as clearly as though he were well acquainted with them he describes their chief characteristic, that of rapid multiplication, and ascribes their life to God.

We must not forget that water teems with life. It is not possible to find water in a natural state or condition, without finding it to be the residence of a host of living things. We see this is true of every drop of sea water, as well as of the fresh streams. This is as true of the alkaline wells in the desert as it is of the sweet springs on the mountain side. The water in the faucet that we drink, or the water in the arsenic spring of Death Valley, is all the same in this respect; every drop of water supports its population of life. This is also true of the saps and juices of plants, the oils and moistures of fruit, leaves, or bark, as well as of the moisture that exudes from man or beast. Every drop of water in nature contains a life colony, unless man has artificially sterilized it.

For the sake of convenience in nomenclature, the biologist calls these tiny creatures "animalcules," but their species and varieties are legion. They are known by name, divided into orders and genera, dissected and classified, and there is an entire science of the protozoa. Even when they are so small that a thousand of them can dwell in a single drop of water without crowding, they differ as much one from another as cows and horses differ from each other. They form an amazing field of research and of study.

Since they are truly *alive,* they offer the same problem to the biologists that elephants or horses offer: where did they come from, and how did they originate as living creatures? They never appear unless there have been progenitors, and they always reproduce each *after its own kind.* No matter how large or how small the creature may be in the world of biology, it never, for a single second, forgets this command of God, as written by Moses. It has been considered by the unlearned in biology that maybe these creatures did not need vital ancestors as the metazoa do, because of the production of the infusoria.

These creatures are the type of protozoa that come as the

result of a hay or grass infusion. If we take a bit of hay, straw, grass, or lettuce and put this vegetation in a bit of water, in a short while the water is teeming with living creatures. Put a few drops of water under the microscope, and it is alive with these engaging little animals. Where do they come from? They were not in the water; for we examined it. They were not on the straw, as they must have moisture in order to live. Whence did they come?

They hatched! These creatures reproduce from what we call "spores," a sort of "egg" which comes from the parent. Some of them indeed do not go to this much trouble. They just break up into small pieces, and each piece goes on living as a new individual! If these small segments of the adult are dried up, they will lie dormant as long as they are dry, but in a few hours will mature in moisture and begin their life cycle all over again. Now these spores ride on the air, they are in and on the dust, and they cling to any type of vegetation. It is an absolute impossibility to find anywhere in nature, vegetation that does not contain myriads of these spores, all ready to "hatch" as soon as they are wet. And when they hatch, they hatch out just exactly what their ancestors always were as far back as they had ancestors! They never evolve, progress, or change into a higher order of protozoa; they remain what they were from the very beginning of time.

The variety of their forms is an amazement to the careful student. Although there are myriads of varieties, they never seem to cross, or confuse their original structure. Thus we see that Paramecium, one of the commonest of the infusia, is shaped roughly like an old slipper, and this is one of the first the student begins to recognize at sight. Euglena is much smaller, and Euvella differs from this again, until the many forms of these tiny creatures amount to a world all by themselves. There is nothing haphazard about all this, for the form is somatic to the variety under consideration, and constantly repeats itself in each new generation without deviation from the

original form. Since certain of these protozoa have been observed for over *two thousand generations,* always reproducing
just as their ancestry had ever been, we have a fairly clear idea
as to what the original of these creatures resembled. Their
forms are geometric, and while they may vary in size, as indeed
all individuals may, they never change the pattern of their
bodies. These forms are graceful, and designers are just beginning to reproduce them in dress goods and wall paper, so
that modern man is going to the microscopic world for new
art forms. New to man, but old indeed before the ark of Noah
sailed the watery waste!

Some of these creatures differ from the others in form, and
some differ from the rest in color or other characteristics, but
there is no confusion in their classification. The order that is
called Rhizopod, for instance, may display as many as five
hundred different body forms, but all announce the fact of
specific creation by their obedience to the command of Genesis: "each after its own kind." Thus we are able to distinguish, classify, and keep in their regular order all the varieties
of these creatures, and man can learn them each from the other by their very appearance.

Other forms of the animalcules differ in their means of
locomotion. One form, such as the Paramecium, is surrounded with a row of cilia, and these by constant motion drive the
creature through the water that is its natural environment.
Another may have one single cilium in the front end, to pull
it through the water much as the propeller of an airship pulls
it through the atmosphere, and another may have the cilium
on the rear, to drive it like the screw of a boat. Still others
have no cilia, or other organs of locomotion, so they move by
an accumulation of ectoplasm!

This method must perhaps be explained for the sake of the
lay-reader, but it is an ingenious method of travel. By the very
fact that protoplasm is auto-contractile, these creatures advance about one-third of themselves ahead in the direction

they wish to journey, and then thrust out another third of their substance by the side of the first advance. Then they simply allow the final third of their substance to flow into the advanced two-thirds and they have traveled through the water by the diameter of their own person!

Some of them have what may pass for "organs" of digestion, in the possession of food vacuoles, by which their prey is assimilated into the substance of the hunting protozoan. Others have no organs of digestion or ingestion, but they eat anyway! By thrusting one-third of their person past the diatom, or whatever else the food object may be, these tiny animals announce their intention of dining. They then thrust another third of themselves past the food object on the other side, and by joining the tips of the advanced sections together, they fold themselves about the prey, and calmly proceed to assimilate the living matter they have thus captured! When the act of "digestion" (if we may so term it) is completed, the hunter opens up and journeys ahead after another tidbit, and spends its life in this activity.

The methods of reproduction among the protodoa are vaied as well. Some kinds reproduce by spores, and some by direct cell division. Some conjugate and some do not, and some simply break up into pieces, each piece quickly becoming a matured adult of its own kind, thus possessing a pseudo-immortality, in that the first one of this kind is still alive, in a sense, in its modern descendants. Certainly they were all listening when God said, as Moses records, that they were to distinguish themselves by "multiplying rapidly!" Their numbers thus became so stupendous that the mind cannot conceive the multitude of them.

Some time ago I was working in the laboratory with one of these species, which lives sixty hours, matures at the age of twelve hours, and every twelve hours reproduces an average of sixty young. I wished to know how many this would result in after twelve months. So I called a friend, a professor of mathematics at our university, and put the problem to him in these terms: If a given protozoan lived sixty hours, and every twelve hours reproduced sixty progeny, who in turn followed this cycle, *how many individuals would there be at the end of one year.*

We can see at a glance that the number would be enormous. Just take the number in the one individual's lifetime for an estimate. A given individual would be parent to 300 children. But when the second group of 60 were spored, that is, when the parent was 24 hours old, the first sixty would each one be presenting the parent with sixty grandchildren, a total of 3,600. Twelve hours later the parent has 60 more direct offspring, but at the same time the first generation is again accounting for 3,600 more grandchildren, while the first 3,600 grandchildren are each having sixty offspring, making 216,000 great-grandchildren to be added to the total. This process of multiplication keeps on until at the death of the first parents, at the age of sixty hours, they leave behind them as mourners some 884,380,200 descendants! How well these creatures obey this dictum that Moses here records! The writer did not have either the patience or the skill to work this problem out in terms of one whole year, but the professor of mathematics, to whom we submitted the problem, replied months later. He said that on the basis of reproduction, this one creature would have left in one year, progeny to the number of 1,318,626, followed by 3,127 yards of ciphers written seven to an inch! I am positive I have no conception of how many that may be, unless we say it is a whale of a lot! How strange that these tiny creatures so willingly obey Moses, when neither ever heard of the other! Or rather let us say, how clearly this demonstrates that Moses *must* have spoken by inspiration; since only God the Creator could have revealed to a man what men did not find out until thousands of years later.

Equally important is the testimony of the fish. After generations of research in the science of ichthyology, no single fact has ever been brought to light that argues against the fact of specific creation of the creatures classified as fish. On the contrary, every fact discovered about these fascinating occupants of the sea strengthens the contention of Moses, that they are the result of God's special work in creation. They range in size from the gigantic Rhynodon typicus down to the tiny Filamentosa, but small or large, rare or common, they agree with an indisputable unanimity on this one point.

They were created!

The first evidence of this is their amazing adaption to their weird environment. This is positive proof of intelligent design. No man could postulate a creature that could live in the water, if he were faced with the necessity of doing so, and had never seen a fish. We would unhesitatingly say that it could not be done; but because we have been more or less familiar with the fish since earliest childhood, we miss the wonder of this strange creation. It is as unreasonable that creatures should live in the water, unless they were designed by Intelligence for that strange environment, as it is that living things be found in the fire. But the fish has a body which shows that careful thought was expended on the solution of this problem.

Their shape is perfect for the realm in which their life is cast. Fish furnish the basic design for most of the speed devices of man. When we needed a vehicle to float on the sea, we made a boat that had a body like a fish, and found it practical for our purpose. When we designed an under-sea craft we made it even more like the fish, and once more it was a success. The mighty Zeppelin that cleaves the atmosphere had the problem of atmosphere pressure to overcome as it moved ahead with stately grace, so we gave that ship of the air the body of a fish. Even the racing auto that shatters records as fast as speeding men can establish them is designed with a body like the fish, and thus is able to overcome the natural forces that would retard its progress. In a word, then, the pressure problem that would be a grievous one to the fish, is solved on the same basis of applied mathematics that man has used for his vehicles; but man learned from the fish!

In their contest with gravity the fish are far ahead of man! Their floating and locomotor apparatuses are alike miracles of design. I have sat and watched fish by the hour, and they in turn have been apparently as interested in me. But I had to remain motionless while I studied their conduct, while they came and went at their own desire. I have had a fish remain motionless while he stared me in the face, seemingly wondering what kind of a queer fish I was! Not able to decide, the fish would try a different point of view. Wonder of wonders! without moving a muscle as far as the observer could decide, the fish quietly, steadily, and easily ascended ten feet or so to look down on the observer, who was in turn being observed. Finding this "bird's eye view" no better, the fish just descended to a lower level and looked up! As far as the observer could tell, not a muscle moved in this course of action, and fish do have the strange power of changing their stratum of dwelling at the dictate of their own fancy.

Man cannot do that, without the aid of some sort of elevator, or else only at the expense of arduous work as he climbs. How different our life would be if we possessed this power! A man would but stand beneath his office window, and by some hidden impulse, lift himself fifty stories above the level of the sidewalk, then calmly drift into his office window, and back out again.

There is no covering that protects the fleshy structure of any living things that compares in perfection to the scales of a fish. The fur, hair, skin, and feathers of the various creatures are all marvelous in design, but none more so than the scales of the fish. They are too perfectly fitted for the performance of their function to be the result of chance. Viewed under the high powers of a compound microscope, the end of the scale that joins the body of the fish rather resembles the structure of the hoof common to the horse family. Thus the flesh of the fish is protected by an adequate armour, and bruises and abrasions are escaped. But the other end of the scale, when thus viewed under the microscope, feathers out to a delicate oilskin jacket to keep its possessor dry! So that the body of the fish is marvelously protected by a watertight covering far superior to the raincoats used by men. There is no pressure so great, no current so swift, or no jet of water so powerful that it can penetrate the "seams" of the raincoat of the fish, because it has no seams! They thus present an evidence of design that is inescapable.

Equally important in our search for the evidence of intelligent and specific creation is the respiratory device of the fish. The free oxygen in the water is all that is available to the denizen of the deep, and there is a complicated problem to be solved in extracting that oxygen and making it serve the needs of the fish. Although the water itself is composed of oxygen to the extent of one-third (water being H_2O), this oxygen cannot be used by the living things that inhabit the water in the same manner as we occupy and use the atmosphere. So the Creator has equipped the fish with a special device called the "gill." It is the plumules of the gill that separate the oxygen from the water; and this principle is the identical one used in the laboratory equipment that is commonly employed for this same purpose! The laboratory machine, of course, is the result of applied intelligence. An inventor reasoned the process through to a successful technique, wrought out his idea in metal, made active by electricity, and the thing works perfectly. Then by the same process of reasoning we deduce that the Great Inventor planned out this method, expressed the idea in living flesh, made it active by the mysterious power of life, and we find the process working in what we ignorantly call nature, as well as it does in the laboratory. But if it is the result of intelligence in one place, there is no escaping the conclusion that the same process is an equal evidence of design elsewhere.

Once more we will contemplate the design manifest in the organs of sight as we see them employed in the Pisces. All fish are under the first law of nature, which is that of self-preservation; and eternal vigilance with them is the very price of life! They are subject to attack from below, above, the front and the rear, and both sides as well! They are sought as food by man, beast, bird, and by their fellows as well, and there is never a minute, awake or asleep, that their lives are safe. If they swim in the depths they are attacked by some nameless monster of the Stygian deep; and if they come to the surface they are the prey of some swooping bird that lives on fish. That is, if they are not captured half way up during their flight to the surface. So the fish has to be able to see every way at once. He cannot take time to turn his head and glance behind as many animals do; he must see all ways at once.

When we study the position of the eyes in the head of the fish, we are delighted to see how well this particular need is met. These organs of vision are so placed that a fish can look ahead, to the rear, up or down, or to either side by merely rolling the eyeballs in a given direction. Thus he is constantly alert and able to survive in the pitiless struggle for existence, which is his life. Could *chance* have thus arranged a perfect equipment for the only creature which has this specific need?

Equally remarkable is the shape of the eye of the fish. The refraction of the light beneath the sea is so different from that in the atmosphere, the visitor from the upper world is at a tremendous disadvantage. So there has been designed for his aid, goggles for under-water work. When the student of the depths descends to his field of observation, he goes equipped with a pair of goggles *that are patterned after the exact shape of the eyeball of the fish!* Thus he not only protects his eyes from the pressure of the water, but adds about thirty feet to the range of his vision. We are very grateful to the able oculist who thus designed and made these goggles; *but who designed them for the fish?*

The powers of magnification are at the disposal of human beings, because some of our fellow men have devoted their lives to the science that deals with vision, and able masters of mathematics have produced optical instruments that make visible to us the smaller things. The fish, however, cannot step into the sales room of such a firm as Bausch and Lomb and purchase a microscope, yet they have vastly more need of this enlarged vision than man. Much of their food is so small that the eye of man cannot even see it, and the smaller fish would starve without magnified vision. So we are elated to find that the eye of the fish magnifies, in exact increasing ratio to the diminishing size of its food! Some of the very small fish that feed on plankton have vision that magnifies as much as six and seven times, and are thus able to find their microscopic prey. Can intelligence escape the conclusion of this thought? If design is seen in the science of magnification as wrought by man, *it is also seen in the handiwork of God!*

We have all seen folks among the world of men who have bi-focal glasses. Their lenses are so constructed that they may read through the lower half of the glass, which magnifies for close work, but they may look at the world through the upper half of the lens, which is designed to aid the vision in distance. How few of us know that the first bi-focal lenses were not made by man, but are found in the very eyeball of a fish!

In Malaysian waters there is a fish that is thus equipped. It is a small fish, about the size of the common sardine, and it is highly prized as food by many creatures. All of the larger fish seek it avidly, men gather it by the basketful; but its worst enemy is found among the birds of the air. There is a small gull that follows the schools of fish as they feed, and swoops from the sky to dart upward again with a beakful of the helpless delicacy.

This little fish feeds on a tiny worm, that is almost too small to be seen by the eye of man, so the fish has to have vision to magnify its prey. Magnification results in restriction of the field of vision, however, so the fish with this type of sight is necessarily short-sighted. On the one hand this fish must be near-sighted to see its food, but at the same time it has to be unusually far-sighted to see its own enemies, the birds. The Creator has met this need in a wonderful way. There is a membrane across the eyeball of this fish that divides the eye into two sections. The bottom half is *near-sighted* and magnifies the food creatures to make them visible to the questing fish; but the upper half of the eyeball is *far-sighted,* and allows the fish thus to escape from the approaching bird! It seems to be a self-evident conclusion, that if the bi-focal glasses used by men are the result of design and intelligence, the bi-focal eyeball of the fish is likewise the result of reason and Creative Mind.

Strange as it may seem, the fish also preach to us the Gospel of the grace of God, and tell us of His marvelous provision for the needs of man. Like the other creatures mentioned on this day, they are called "good," and it is the universal consensus of human opinion that they *are* good. Indeed, myriads of human beings would die but for this food, as it is all they have to eat. Indeed, the fish were definitely created to be of service and pleasure to man. In the record of the twenty-eighth verse of Genesis one, it is specifically stated that man is to have domain over the fish, as also he is to have control over the rest of nature. It is a noteworthy fact that the mouth of a fish is designed for the hook, as the hoof of the horse seems designed to submit to the blacksmith's nail! There is no more pain or physical suffering to the hooked fish than there is to the shod horse; provided, of course, the fish is not allowed to swallow the hook. With no nerves and ganglia in the mouth to transmit pain, there can be no real humanitarian reason why fish should not be captured by the method commonly

known as angling, and the writer boldly admits that he is an
ardent fisherman, and desires to thank the good God that He
made this sport possible!

We are somewhat surprised to note that the fish are mentioned in the Bible thirty-three times in connection with the
affairs of men! In the eighth Psalm they are spoken of as
serving him; they do indeed aid man in many surprising ways.
The most unusual probably being the fish that was host to
Jonah for the memorable three days and nights. Incidentally,
this was a fish, and not a whale, as the author has shown in
Volume One of this series.

Fish are amazingly prominent in the ministry of the Lord
Jesus Christ. So much so that they constitute a considerable
mystery in His Record. For years we have pondered over the
significance of fish in His works, with very little light having
been shed upon the problem so far. They enter into His teachings, they are used to show His power over the nature whose
God He is, and they portrayed His deity to the early Christian.

The first direct reference that Jesus made to fish seems to be
in the seventh chapter of Matthew, verse ten. To show with
graphic force the care of God over those who love and trust
Him, Jesus illustrates His teaching with these words:

"Or what man is there of you, whom if his son ask bread,
will he give him a stone? Or if he ask a fish, will he give him
a serpent? If ye then, being evil, know how to give good gifts
unto your children, how much more shall your Father Which
is in Heaven give good things to them that ask Him?" Herein
is illustrated the nature of God toward those who receive
Him as a father; He cares for them. As fish were a most impor
tant item in the diet of Palestine in the day of our Lord, He
naturally uses this type of food to point His teaching. Even
more significant is the actual use made of this order of life in
His miracles and ministry. In the list of Apostles whom He
chose, Simon and James and John were commercial fishermen.

Jesus makes His appearance in their lives very simply and quietly, with an announcement that He is later to possess them in full surrender. Thus ever He seems to come! Desiring a place to teach the multitude where they cannot crush Him in their eagerness to hear, He enters Simon's boat and asks that it may be pushed a little way out from the shore. With that respect for a teacher that characterizes the oriental mind, Simon responds, and the Master sits down to teach.

When He had finished His message to the listening crowd, He turned to Simon and suggested that they cast their nets for a haul. But Peter, worn out with a fruitless night of toil, despondently replies that it is useless; there are no fish there. However, on the command of the Teacher, he obeys, and the catch is so great he needs must call for help. His three partners come running to his aid, bringing their second boat, and the catch is so great that both boats are swamped with the load! Then Peter does a strange thing: although he is a devout Jew, who would cheerfully die rather than bow his knee to any but Deity, he falls on his knees to this man and says, "Depart from me, *Oh Lord!* for I am a sinful man!" Student of nature that he was, Peter knew that only God could command the fishes in this manner, and Jesus thus presents His credentials to these three, who afterward left their nets to follow Him.

In the record of the fourteenth chapter of Matthew we have the miracle of the feeding of the multitude. There is no *natural* explanation of this miracle; it passes the bounds of human understanding. How many people were fed that day no man can say, the record merely states that there were five thousand men, besides all the women and children. When Jesus performed this great miracle, He fed this mass of humanity with five loaves (flat cakes) of barley bread and *two fish*. In the repetition of this wonder, when He later fed the four thousand (again counting the men only) He had seven loaves and *a few fish*.

We note this same evidence introduced in the record of the seventeenth chapter of Matthew, where Peter is asked by the officers if his Master does not pay the half shekel of the temple. In the thirtieth chapter of Exodus this matter is fully set forth, in the command to pay the ransom price at the time of the census. When the count was made of the nation, the rule was that each soul should pay a half shekel to redeem his soul from pride in the growth of the people, and to turn his thoughts to God. The text says, "The rich may not pay more, and the poor shall not pay less, than the half shekel." It is not, then, the amount that is of interest in the study, but the fact that the price of salvation is the same for all classes!

So when Peter was challenged by the authorities for the payment of this sum, he replied that they would pay it, and then came to the Lord to see if he had answered correctly. In the following conversation Jesus takes the opportunity to emphasize the unique position of those who are the sons of God by virtue of their faith in the Lord Jesus Christ, and He asks Peter, "Of whom do the kings of this earth receive tribute; from their own sons or from strangers?" (This word here rendered stranger is the Greek word "allotrios"; and it means the subjects of another.) Peter replied, "From strangers"; and the Lord Jesus said, "The sons therefore are free. But in order that we cause the officers no offense, go to the sea, let down your hook, and take up the first fish you catch. Open his mouth, and there you will find a whole shekel. That take, and pay to the temple for Me and thee." So the fish enters miraculously into the ministry of the Lord once more, in the impression made upon Peter of his sonship with God because of his faith in Jesus as his Lord.

Even after the resurrection of the Lord from the dead the fish continue to speak. When He appeared to His disciples, they were terrified, supposing that He was a ghost or a spirit. In order to convince them that He was actually risen from the dead, He took some cooked fish and a bit of honeycomb and ate it before their eyes. This physical action convinced them, and they went forth to give their testimony of the resurrection from the dead.

Later we see the risen Christ meeting the five fishermen by the side of the sea, when they had gone back to their old craft —Peter, Thomas, Nathanael, James, and John had once more toiled all night, and had caught nothing. At dawn they saw the risen Saviour standing by the bank, and heard Him say, "Children, have ye caught anything?" They replied, "No." He then told them to cast again on the right side, and they caught so great a draft of fishes that they were not able to draw in the nets. John then cried to Peter, "It is the Lord!" Peter, in the excitement of the moment, sprang into the water and made his way to the shore, and the others slowly followed him. When they got there, they saw that Jesus had provided food, for on a fire that burned there He had laid fish and bread to eat with them.

Some day I hope to understand the exact significance of fish in the ministry of Jesus, but now I have only this one faint glimmering of light; it may have to do with the Adamic covenant. In the creation hour God gave Adam dominion over all things, including fish. He lost this dominion in the sin and the fall, and man has had nature for an enemy ever since! In all the world of nature the fish are the most difficult things for man to train to obey him, so that when Jesus came as *the last Adam*, He demonstrated His power in this covenant by the obedience of the fish to Him.

In the early history of the Christian Church, the fish was the symbol of the believer as the cross is today. Men wore it on their person to denote their faith, and in the times of persecution, when men were imprisoned and slain for the crime of worshipping the Lord Jesus, they would paint this sign of the fish over their places of meeting to advise the stranger where to attend divine worship. In the catacombs at Rome the visitor still sees the fish that were painted there as a sign of

Christianity. The fish was even used as a sign and a password among the early Christians, that they might know each other when they met.

The reason for this is the spelling of the word fish in the Greek text. This word is "ichthus" and in the Greek characters has this unusual significance: when we write the word in Greek, "JESUS CHRIST, GOD AND SAVIOUR" (Iesous Xristos Theos u Soter) the first letter of each word spells the Greek word fish. So the early Christians *who believed as all true Christians believe* that Christ is indeed GOD AND SAVIOUR, adapted this word and sign to their need, and used it to signify their adoration of Him. We may not wear this sign on our person today, but in our hearts we bear the same glad faith, and happy is that man who sees in the work of the Fifth Day of Genesis not only the record of creation, but a forecast of the Saviour as well.

The Hum of Wings

CHAPTER NINE

The Hum of Wings

WHEN MOSES records with that significant brevity that characterizes all his inspired utterances, "And God created . . . every winged bird after its kind" he gave the only intelligent, scientific, and acceptable explanation that the world has ever received for the mystery met with in the realm of ornithology! Having considered in the preceding chapter the section of the first chapter of Genesis that deals with the creatures of the water, we now come to the contrasting type of life, mentioned as created on this same day, which dwells not in the water, but in the air. In a certain very definite sense of resemblance, the birds and the fish belong together in the one record. Birds may be said to swim through the air and fish to fly through the water. Equally they are equipped to resist the law of gravity, and able to live by their very nature in the environments which tolerate men for only brief hours, and then often exact the death penalty for his intrusion.

So in this paragraph of the creation chapter, namely, from the twentieth verse to the twenty-third, we see again the proof of the inspiration of the record, and its wonderful significance in the figures of salvation. The first we see in the marvelous fidelity to scientific accuracy, as we know it in the exact knowledge of the present day; and the second we see in the pictures of the coming Saviour that the Old Testament draws with the figures of this day. Once more we trace the proof of Mosaic accuracy, in that the winged things all show design in creation, and design cannot be separated from the thought and the person of the Designer. Birds, especially, cry aloud this testimony.

First of all, in their very shapes and forms. The birds are all *living wedges*, perfectly formed to cleave the atmosphere that is at the same time their sphere of living and their handicap. There is as much resistance, relatively speaking, to the progress of the bird's body through the atmosphere as is offered by the water to the passage of the fish. But the first thing we note in the structure of the body of the bird is the perfect adaptation of its entire form for the conquest of its sphere of motion. A bird in flight, from the point of its extended beak to the wind-splitting tip of its tail, offers the most perfect example of streamlining to be found in the entire realm of biology. So perfect is this design, that after generations of human wisdom and intellect have been applied to the problem, we have no man-made vehicle as wonderfully equipped to resist the retarding effect of atmospheric pressure as is the body of a bird. If no man had ever seen a bird in flight, and yet had the opportunity to dissect and study the body of one that had died, his conclusion must inevitably be, "Surely, this strange creature was intended to dwell in the air; it is perfectly designed for flight."

Equally significant is the overcoming of the law of gravity, by all the feathered and winged creatures. How is it that a great living creature, in some cases attaining a weight of twenty pounds or more, can float in the air like the down of the thistle? It is designed for that very purpose! It testifies to this fact in many ways, chiefly in that it is a miniature fire balloon.

In our childhood days we celebrated the Fourth of July by making these fire balloons. We took light and strong slivers of bamboo, shaped them to the general outline of a gigantic pear, and covered the frame with tissue paper, bright of color, light, and strong. At the bottom of the balloon we gathered all our "ribs" together in a wire ring, and to that ring we fastened a sponge soaked in alcohol or benzine. When the sponge was ignited, the heated air filled the balloon and it ascended grandly into the air, to stay as long as the sponge continued to

burn, or to come down perchance in some farmer's hayfield!
(Which may be the reason that they passed out of style!)

A bird operates on somewhat that same basic principle. Its
body temperature is much higher than that of the mammals
and is designed to contain air-spaces in many parts and sections of the anatomy, even in some of the quills. The bones
and "solid" parts are of the "hollow structure" type, and
weight is ruthlessly reduced by any means at every possible
point. When the body of the bird is filled with air, this is
heated by the body temperature far above the normal atmospheric point, and buoyancy is the result. Does not this argue
design? The one order of life which requires this structure
possesses it.

Yet the birds that float like oil on the surface of the water,
can also descend like a stone into its depths. There is no
stronger evidence of design anywhere in nature than this. Let
us observe the friendly, pert, and entrancing bird called the
ouzel (pronounced oo-z'l) that is found along the mountain
streams. This bird is peculiar to the mountains of the Pacific
Coast, and is always found where the water is the fastest and
where falls and rapids dash and chuckle in the splash of foam.
They build their nests under the brink of a fall, and precede
the fishermen down the stream in friendly association, darting
from rock to rock and bowing their compliments at every
landing.

They are the most buoyant birds in all the records of
ornithology. They float on the surface like grease, seeming
to ride above the water, instead of partly in the water, as is
the case of the duck or goose. It seems impossible to sink
these birds, but the observer, watching from a hidden point
of advantage above, is startled to see the ouzel suddenly
descend into the swift water like a leaden sinker! There this
strange creature of three worlds, the land, the air, and the
water, calmly *walks* about on the bottom, as though it were
made of iron instead of flesh and bones. When the feeding

bird has filled its beak with all it can hold, it wades out on the bank, shakes itself, swallows its mouthful of food, and a few seconds later is calmly floating like smoke on the surface of the stream!

This conduct is possible only because of the special equipment of the ouzel, which argues for the fact of its specific creation. The bird is provided with a special muscular apparatus that instantly exhausts the air from its body, and gives it the weight needed to sink in swift water, and to stay down! Then when it comes to the bank and fills its body again with air, it instantly regains the lost buoyancy, and floats away on the rushing stream as though it never did anything else! To float like a cork or sink like a stone, at will, requires designing that is at present past the ability of man, and no human could design or conceive such a creature as the ouzel!

A great deal has been said about the varying faces of the human kind, but one of the most fascinating studies in all nature is the multiplicity of countenances among the birds. Every face in the bird world is designed for a purpose. For instance, how could the toucan crack a nut if it had a face like a canary bird, or how could a canary bird pick up the minute seeds that constitute its diet if it in turn had a face like a toucan? Or, if, by accident, the pelican were born with the face of a parrot, the pelican so unfortunately equipped would quickly starve to death! How wonderful that the pelican, nature's best fisherman, has at birth not only a fish net for a face, but a cupboard to hold his food as well! There is evidence of design in the faces of birds.

Here is one creature we call a chicken, and its problem is to pick up seeds, scraps, bugs, and worms on the dry land. It has a beak perfectly fitted to that purpose. But the duck, on the other hand, has a different problem. It must descend to the bottom of the pond, and here dredge its food from the mud and ooze on the floor of the environment it loves best

of all. Strange, is it not, that the duck should be miserable
away from the water, and the chicken should perish in the
water, if they were not each designed for their separate
spheres of dwellings? But what a tragic mistake it would be
if a chicken had the bill of a duck, and the duck had the beak
of a chicken! Truly design is manifested here if intelligence
will but observe, and Moses must have been right when he
said that God created each winged thing after its own kind!

We have a shore bird on the Pacific Coast that perfectly
exemplifies this evidence of design in the face of the bird.
Its principal article of diet is a large worm which lives in a
hole in the sand, just between the level of the two tides.
When the tide is out this bird may be seen feeding along the
shore, and its problem is as complicated as its method is
ingenious. The worm that is its food lives at the bottom of
a hole, which hole is the exact diameter of the long beak of
this bird. The face of this bird is just long enough to fill
this hole and touch the worm at the bottom. But when the
bird's face fills the hole, and it can touch the worm, it cannot
open its beak and grab its victim, as the sides of the hole
have firmly grasped the entire beak for almost its length!
So down at the tip end of the bird's face, about three-eighths
of an inch from the end, there is a hinged flap, exactly like
the long forceps that the doctor uses to grasp certain tissues,
or to insert a gauze plug in a difficult place. This hinge opens
independently, and although the rest of the face remains
closed, the bird can use these forceps at the end of its face to
grasp firmly its prey. Incidentally, it is also saved from getting
a mouthful of sand!

When the worm is firmly grasped by the hinged portion of
the end of the beak, it is withdrawn from the hole, washed
off in the shallow water at the edge of the tide, and engulfed
at one gulp, by the only bird that has the specialized apparatus
with which to capture it! Search the entire world of nature,
and no other creature has this peculiar and particular type

of face, and no other creature needs it, as this is the one bird that feeds on these worms. If this does not show design, and thus creation, we are at a loss how to account for this marvelous equipment just where it is specially needed.

The feet of birds, as well as their faces, also argue for design. If the savage beak of the hawk or eagle testifies that it was designed for the eating of meat, no less do the claws that can hold the struggling prey bear this same record. The feet of the birds are adapted to, or designed for, the very type of creatures on which they are found.

Notice, as an instance, the feet of the duck. Only rarely does he walk on the land, by preference he swims about in the water, floating in comfort where most birds would perish. Because he is faced with the problem of propulsion through the water, he is equipped with webbed feet. At the end of each leg he has an ingenious paddle, or oar, to drive him in the direction in which he desires to go. Either on the surface or down underneath, the duck is able to proceed about his business because of his webbed feet. Query: did he take to the water because he had webbed feet, or did he get webbed feet because he took to the water? It is evident at once that the latter cannot be the case, for what would the duck have done in the water while he was getting or developing these webbed feet? Also, the down of a duck that keeps him safe in the water must have provided him in the very hour of his origin, or the water would have been as fatal to him as it is to a chicken today! It is apparent to the most superficial observer, that if the duck appears at the very start with webbed feet, he must have been created for the water. Thus again we see design.

The chicken, on the other hand, would be sadly handicapped by having webbed feet. Not intended for the water, this creature makes its living, literally, by scratching. Of what use would webbed feet be to a bird that has to scratch and turn the soil for a living? Viewed from this angle, the armed toes of the chicken are perfect for this purpose, and design seems to be established again! If the matter of life equipment is left to chance, how fortunate that the duck and the chicken each got the exact sort of feet they need!

There is another bird, called variously "mud-hen," "Hochia" and "coot" which is familiar to every frequenter of the swamps. It is a bird with black plumage, white beak, and yellowish-green legs. Sometimes it may be seen quietly swimming about in the water and again may be found feeding upon the bank. It spends its time as its fancy dictates or food supplies determine, either in the water or on the land.

For swimming it needs some sort of webs, and yet as it feeds on the land it would not be able to run and scratch if it had the webs of a duck. So to fit this special case, God in creation gave to the American coot webs that *fold tightly around its toes* when it walks on the land, and it is thus able to scratch or run like a chicken. But when this coot takes to the water, its webs automatically unfold, and it is thus able to swim as no chicken ever could. Incidentally, it is also equipped with the waterproof covering of the duck, and this again argues that it was created especially for this strange double existence; half of its life simulating a duck, and the other half a chicken! But it is neither duck nor chicken, it is a coot, exactly as the Lord designed it to be. So plain is its own testimony to this fact, that it is not necessary to give it the gifts of speech; its evidence is conclusive from its very structure. It belongs among the witnesses for design in creation, and cannot be refuted by any opposition infidelity may produce!

Every fisherman, of course, grasps at once the peculiar problem of the fishing birds, such as the kingfish. Who has not struggled with his heart in his mouth, when a prize trout has dropped off the hook and flops at the very edge of the stream, seeking escape! What a hopeless task to try to grasp a wet fish with wet hands, and hang on! The common solution of the problem is for the fisherman to fall on said fish and hug it to the fisherman's bosom; but a bird cannot do it that way!

Fortunately the bird is not under such necessity. Creation has given the fishing birds hooks that are barbed, and never allow the prey to escape, once these talons have fastened into the victim. In some of these birds there are rows of hooks on the back of the claw that match serrations on the inside of the opposite claw, and all of them have the power to grasp and not let go. We cannot help but note that if the birds had to evolve this apparatus over thousands of years of slow "improvement" the first fishers would have starved to death before their apparatus appeared; but if the first fishing birds came so equipped, it was design, creation, intent, and the case stands attested.

It is strange, is it not, how slow we are sometimes to observe some very common phenomenon? The first time the writer ever observed the fact that the long-legged fishing birds had legs which were hinged at the knees so they work opposite to the expected direction, it struck him as so humorous that he followed the long, gangling, solemn crane for hours just enjoying the odd sight. Of course, this is what we would expect from a wader, but only after observing one in action did the significance of this fact dawn upon the observer. Instead of the knees bending so the lower leg folds to the rear, these large waders bend at the knee joint the other way. They bend the lower leg up and to the front, instead of to the back, thus mechanically watching where they put their foot in front of them as they quietly make their way through the shallows in the eternal quest for food. Ponder for a moment the happy fact that the one class of birds that could so obediently use this odd articulation all possess it, and nowhere else in the living orders is it met with. Design again!

How could human ingenuity solve the totally different problem of the bird that is called the canary? It must perch, asleep or awake, on a tiny swaying twig, that presents a problem in balance difficult to solve. We may conceive how the bird could maintain its equilibrium during the waking hours, but how in the name of acquired characteristics could the sleeping bird remain secure when the trees toss in the wind? The perch is small in diameter, the pull of gravity is relentless even on the birds, and the perch moves from point to point ceaselessly while the bird sleeps. How is this done?

There is a system of musculature which locks the bird's toes around the perch, and this system takes hold as soon as the bird alights. By a wonderful dispensation of Providence, this system of muscles locks itself in the periods of sleep, and only in conscious moments can the bird let go! So that no matter how the wind may blow and the perch may sway, the creature so provided cannot fall or be tossed off, and the quiet of sleep is made as safe as the moments of volition when the whole creature is wide awake. No wonder the writer of the Book could say, "How marvelous are His judgments, and His ways past finding out!" Even if He had not been pleased to reveal Himself to man as He has in His Word we would see the fact of His power and intelligence in such marvelous arrangements as this!

If the mysterious force called "instinct" (for want of a better name) is indeed, as we believe it to be, *imparted wisdom*, the birds possess this wisdom to a marked degree. The reader may recall that in a former generation, the eminent Bernoilli propounded a problem that for a while no man was able to answer. Then Newton and Leibnitz, working independently of each other, arrived at the solution simultaneously, and both worked out the same answer. The question was, "At what angle of descent would a falling body descend at the utmost rapidity?"

Because of various physical factors, it is apparent at once it will *not* be the perpendicular. Because of the inclination of the earth off the true perpendicular, the rotation on its axis and the consequent atmosphere motion and pressure, a falling body on the angle of the perpendicular would be at least slightly retarded. Any solid object descending under the force of gravity, builds up increasing air pressure just as the piston of an air compression operates in a cylinder. Consequently when an object has fallen a certain distance, it attains a maximum speed and increase of velocity, and from that point on is inhibited by the factor of increased air pressure. A falling body, however, that descends in a path that follows the arch of a cycloid, seems to allow escape of this air pressure and thus attains the utmost possible speed.

Every bird of prey in the world of ornithology strikes at that exact angle! Only two men of science in all Europe were able to solve this problem in their day, yet all the hunting birds are born with this knowledge as a part of their essential equipment! How can we account for this marvelous fact, if not on the basis of creation! The God who designed the entire order of the universe, who established its laws and gave it momentum, He alone could have created feathered creatures who possessed the solution of the problems of physics in their imparted wisdom, ages before men even dreamed of these problems. And with the world of fact upon which to draw, one need not hesitate to defend that thesis in debate before the most learned societies the sons of men can organize.

"So God CREATED every winged thing, . . . and God saw that it was good." How true that is, man is just beginning to learn. Birds are among the best friends that man possesses. Nothing alive in the orders of nature so faithfully serves men as they go about their daily affairs, as do the birds. It may as well be admitted first as last, that the real battle for survival is between man and the insect world. Although many of the winged insects are truly the friends of man, there are many, many types of insects that are his worst enemies. One year a pest of this nature destroys the spinach crop, the next year it is the cotton that suffers from the boll weevil. Today it is the fruit fly that threatens the orange groves, and tomorrow it may be the apple crop that faces destruction. Almost everything that man eats or wears, of a vegetable nature, is threatened at one time or another by insect enemies.

The birds constitute man's first line of defense in the war for existence. It is here that man will agree, indeed, with the writing of Moses, that the birds are good. For the very reason that hunger drives them, if for no other, the feathered folk wage ceaseless war on the insect world, and thus ally themselves on the side of man. They ask no wages and demand no recompense; they labor incessantly to keep down the numbers of the enemy, and prove their value and goodness in the performance of their natural labors.

In one of our Western states, the authorities got excited at one time because the Western linnet was found to be eating fruit buds. The cry was raised that they were enemies of the fruit grower, and they were taken off the protected list of song birds, and for some time it was lawful to shoot them in the orchards. Then one of the insect pests began to thrive and multiply, and it was found that although the linnets did ruin an occasional bud, they more than compensated for this minor assessment by subduing this particular insect as a matter of course. The birds are again protected in that state, and indeed are counted the most worthy of citizens; thus demonstrating the wisdom of allowing the balance of nature to remain the way it was ordained in the beginning. It is folly for man to interfere in this balance of power.

Time will not permit the enumeration of all the ways the birds prove to be good in their relation to men, but consider the ever important matter of food. How many birds do we eat? From the mighty Canadian Honker down to the miniature quail, man has a fondness for the flesh of the birds. These creatures, then, which feed the starving body, protect the crops, decorate the person, make the arrow fly straight or provide the softest of beds for tired man, are indeed the friends of man in all that they do; they minister to his wants physically and preach grace to him spiritually!

Wonderful as these facts may be, we must not forget that there are other winged things besides the birds. The world of entomology must be accounted for on this day as well as that of ornithology, and all the winged things show the same evidence of design that is displayed by the birds. For the sake of brevity, we will condense all this evidence to the record of one creature, and for the entire winged entomology the bee will testify.

If there is one living thing more than any other which attests the fact of specific creation, this one is the bee. No evolutionist has any very high regard for the bee, as the evolutionist is stung every time he gets on this subject! The idea that specific organs naturally arise in response to a certain need is absolutely refuted by the bee. This strange creature presents so many odd oppositions to organic evolution that only the theory of specific creation can account for its presence.

The law of Mendel states that in each individual there may be found the characteristics that are in the two immediate ancestors, either recessive or dominant; but the worker bee has characteristics and physiological equipment that are not found in *either* the father or the mother! The worker bee is not only equipped to collect honey (which neither the queen nor the drone can do), but it also has the wax apparatus that is essential to the building of the hive cells, to contain that honey. The male (the drone) and the female (the queen) who are the progenitors of these workers are never thus equipped.

As the worker bees labor away in their hive, the "sweat" that exudes from between their body plates condenses into "wax" and is molded against the hard body plates by the foot of the bee, shaped like a trowel and designed to be used this way. When the wax is formed to suit the purpose of the tiny builder it is cut off by the "scissors" and picked up on the "trowel," and then laid into place as a mason plants his materials in constructing a house. *None of the essential physiology* for this process is possessed by either the father or mother of the worker bee; how can Mendelism account for this? *Creation* seems to be the only answer. The real case, however, seems to hinge on the possession by the worker of a special arrangement to cleanse its breathing apparatus, that makes the continuity of a bee's life possible. Without this device the bee would die. This matter was recently brought to the attention of the world, when a clever biologist published an article in one of the highest class monthly magazines, entitled, *"Evolution Goes to Pieces on a Bee's Knees!"*

This article was not only ingenious, but accurate and timely as well.

The author reviewed the fact that evolution accounts for all changes and differences under the theory that a specific need results in the production of a specific organ to meet that need, and thus the species arrive. But the specific need of the bee is to continue to breathe! As this busy little worker crawls down into the flower in search of honey, its breathing device is plugged tight with pollen, and the bee is in grave danger of perishing.

To meet this need, there are on the knees of a bee, brushes made of clusters of stiff hair, with which the bee cleans out its breathing apparatus, and is able to draw a full breath and go back into the pollen-laden tunnel after more load. Thus the bee survives.

The conclusion of the matter is this: if this organ was produced to respond to this need, then the first bee, not having this essential organ, would have perished by asphyxiation, and the species would have perished at the beginning. But if the brushes were put there in anticipation of that need (as they certainly must have been), then that is creation; forethought, design. So evolution goes to pieces on the knees of a bee!

In like manner all the winged things have some important testimony to give in the matter of specific creation, and the

case of the insects that fly is similar to that of every other order in the natural realm. For a while the protagonists of the
theory of evolution fondly hoped that their case would be
strengthened by the mutations of the fruit fly, Drosophila.
Under control in laboratory experiments, the various types of
the fruit fly respond to the direction of the experimenter by
the production of many odd sports and freaks. Changes occur
in the color of the eye, the shape and size of the wings, the
position and shape of the legs, and so on without apparent
end. This mutation is hopefully advanced by the exponent of
evolution as a proof of the method by which development
occurs eventually to the extent of the appearance of a new
species, but the demonstration has lately collapsed.

It is found that the results obtained in the laboratory never
occur in the wild state of Drosophila, and that these mutations
are freaks. Even if they *did* occur naturally, this would not
constitute a demonstration of the truth of evolution, as nothing but Drosophila ever came from these experiments. And a
fruit fly is still a fruit fly, whether its eyes are brown or blue,
or even if one eye is green and the other one pink! Until mutation of the Drosophila actually results in transmutation,
evolution is not helped or sustained in these genetic experiments. But when a theory is as sick and feeble as this one,
even a *rubber* crutch is better than none at all!

Every butterfly that flutters on the sun-lit air, every wasp
that manufactures paper to build its home, every moth that
seeks the flame, every beetle that buzzes by on his daily affairs;
in short, every creature that travels on wings cries as he goes
by, "Amen to Moses!" Their testimony is, without a single
exception, a united voice for the proof of the fact of specific
creation as they continue to obey the command of the fifth
day, "Each after its own kind!"

Like all the other creatures of God, the orders of life that
appear here have spiritual significance as well as scientific;
they testify to the grace of God in one way and another. "Hon-

ey in the rock" is to us a poetic phrase, but to the ancient dweller in the Holy Land it was a literal fact. Indeed, in the Old Testament the land of Palestine is nineteen times described as a land of milk and honey. This substance was an important article of diet to the people of that day, and the phrase we are considering comes from the fact that in a country where trees were scarce, to say the least, the wild bees made their hives in the crevasses of the rocks. So that it was a literal fact that they could in that place "suck honey out of the rock."

In the eighty-first Psalm, David, speaking for God, reminds the people that God led them out of bondage in Egypt, and that they then turned away from Him and walked after their own lusts. God expresses here His divine regret that the people had turned away from Him, and the Psalm concludes with the three-fold blessing that would have come to Israel if they had turned to the Lord: their enemies would have been subdued, the unbelieving would have been converted, and as a temporal blessing to match the spiritual, He would have fed them with the finest of the wheat, and satisfied them with honey out of the rock! This latter blessing, of course, is possible only as the bees labor to fulfill the purpose of their creation, and serve man.

There is also a symbolic meaning to this phrase, as we see from Psalm nineteen, verse ten. Here the inspired Psalmist describes the commands and judgments of God and says, "More to be desired are they than gold, yea, than much fine gold; sweeter also than honey and the honey comb!" How few of us agree with the Psalmist that the Words of God are more precious than gold! There have been some, a noble company indeed, who gave up all that they had in defense of that Word, sacrificing wealth and lands, home and life itself because they agreed with this writer. But their tribe seems on the wane today, when the Book is so little prized that the average man will not even defend it from the assaults of the ignorant and ungodly in classroom and pulpit alike. Happy indeed is that man who can say as David did in the Psalm numbered one hundred and nineteen: "How sweet are thy Words unto my taste, yea sweeter than honey to my mouth."

Thus by analogy we have come to apply this phrase to the person of the Saviour, and to the blessing of salvation which He brings. So our modern hymn expresses it in these simple but poetic words:

> "Oh my brother, do you know the Saviour?
> He is wondrous, kind and true,
> He's the Rock of your salvation;
> There's honey in the Rock for you."

There *is* honey in the Rock for the believer in the Lord Jesus Christ, but of course each man must gather it for himself. But how natural that we should begin to discuss a creature (in the case of the bee) and end by thinking of the Creator. This is the entire purpose of all creation; that it may testify to God and His goodness, and turn men's thoughts to Him. Not only do "the heavens declare the glory of God," but the earth praises Him as well.

The greatest message is conveyed, however, by the birds. They are present in the Bible to such an extent that it may be said that their song is woven through the entire warp and woof of the structure of this Book. They are mentioned in the various books of the Bible no less than one hundred and seventy-seven times. They portray the helpless dependence of man on God; they picture for us God's faithful care of man; they stand in one picture as the lost who are saved and again they appear as a type of the Saviour. They picture with equal beauty the person of the Christian, and the power and presence of Him who makes us His. They are associated with man from the time of his creation to the finish of his redemption. The entire record of the human race is accompanied by the hum and the beat of wings!

The birds were in Eden, when our first parents dwelt in the bliss that is possible only to those whose lives are entirely well-pleasing to God. They softly sang in the cool of the eve when the Creator and His creature communed in the gloaming, and their twittering voices were the choir that accompanied Adam's song of praise. They appeared in Eden the day before Adam was placed there, and when Man first opened his eyes on the wonders of creation, the brilliant plumage of the birds in flight was one of the first sights to greet his vision, as their song first delighted his ear. Like all the other folk of the wild, Adam was given dominion over them, and with gladness they served him. Indeed, the birds still have that spirit of friendship toward man, and where man will allow it they dwell with him in peace and content. Who has not fed the pigeons in some center of human habitation; and even in the wildest woods man may in time train the birds to eat from his hand.

They were present when man sinned and fell, and lost his dominion over this natural world. Their pitiful cries heralded the fall of creation's natural lord, and they have sung in the minor ever since. When the judgment of God struck the ancient world, the world that then was, the birds accompanied Noah in his journey in the ark, and lightened the dreary year of drifting, with their songs. Indeed, when Noah desired to know the extent of the recession of the waters, it was a bird, the raven, which he first released, and when the raven failed to return, the dove followed it as man's messenger.

If it be contended that the raven was a poor servant of Noah, and utterly failed in his trust when he refused to return to the ark, let us in justice remember that he expiated that error when he faithfully fed the prophet Elijah in the wilderness. Under the command of God it was this wild bird of the heavens that brought to the prophet his daily bread, and kept his life safe. How strange is the cycle of events here revealed: for the ravens, the birds that in the case of Elijah *fed man,* will in the day of the battle of Armageddon *feed upon man!* For as the ravens were present in the first judgment that God visited upon sinful man, so they will be present in the last judgment to come upon flesh, because of its sin.

In the types of the Scripture, the birds appear as the picture of the Saviour. In the first chapter of Leviticus God gives Israel the law of the burnt offerings, and three types of creature are acceptable. Cattle from the herds, sheep from the flocks, or a pair of turtledoves or young pigeons. It is ever true of God that He never demands of man more than he is able to bring, so in the case of the man who is not able to bring an animal to represent the shed blood that brings salvation, the birds were to be the substitute.

Indeed, this is expressly stated in the fourteenth chapter of Leviticus, where the sin-offering and the burnt-offering are specified; the Lord specifically states, "And if he be poor, and cannot get so much . . ." the two birds may be substituted. One of the birds is slain and its blood spilled by the altar, as was customary, but the other was to be dipped in blood and released. In this the student of types sees the two-fold aspect of Christ's salvation; for it is stated in Romans, the fourth chapter, that "He was delivered for our offenses, and was raised again for our justification." So God has not forgotten to make of this order as well the substitutes for the trusting sinner, and the birds not only sing of the grace of God, they thus portray it as well.

How apt seems the lament of Jesus in the light of this fact. It seems that the saddest cry this earth ever heard was when the Creator of all things looked into the darkening face of gathering night and said: ". . . the birds of the air have their nests; but I, the Son of Man, have no place to lay My head!" Infinite in its yearning, it inclines every true man to reply, "Come into my heart, Lord Jesus!" that we may thus in the words of the song compensate a little (oh, *such* a little!) for the neglect men ever showed Him who was their Saviour. He came as a bird to feed on the bounty of God, not of men, and as the bird of the sin-offering He gave His blood for those who could not afford or provide the price of salvation, so that in Him the poorest as well as the richest might find salvation.

Thus the birds become as well the type of the saved. In the graphic teachings of Jesus He calls attention to this fact in His own incomparable fashion, when He twice likens the believer to the humblest of birds, which is the sparrow. In the tenth chapter of Matthew He says, "Are not two sparrows sold for a penny? And one of them shall not fall to the ground without your Father . . . Fear not therefore, ye are of more value than many sparrows."

Some have fancied a contradiction in the text because the Lord repeats this lesson again in the twelfth chapter of Luke, and says, "Are not five sparrows sold for two pennies? and not one of them is forgotten before God." Indeed, the questioner who brought this to my attention asked, "Now, which is the correct translation, and what is the price of sparrows?" The answer is, both are right. We are familiar with this method in our modern markets; apples may be five cents apiece, but at the same time sell six for twenty-five cents! Thus it was with sparrows; they were so cheap that two sold for a penny, but if a customer would buy two pennies worth, one sparrow was thrown in for nothing. And it is this *one* sparrow, too cheap to count in the transaction, that typifies God's care for us. We are the odd sparrow, but if God remembers the humble and insignificant, the worthless and the forgotten, how much more will He remember those who are His children by right of the new birth?

The dove of the Scripture is the fitting symbol of that blessed Third Person of the Trinity that is the Holy Spirit. In the third chapter of Matthew the writer records the baptism of Jesus, and says that the Holy Spirit, in the form of a dove, descended from Heaven and rested upon the Son of God at that time and during that ceremony. So then we have this definite revelation and authority for saying that the dove is the type of the Spirit of God. The perfection of this picture is seen when it is noted that the dove of the Orient has no gall. That which stands in all languages as the symbol of bitterness is left out of this creature, and it thus logically becomes the type of Him who brings to men the sweetness of the grace of God.

So in the tenth chapter of Matthew the Saviour charges His followers to be as wise as serpents, but as harmless as doves! This then is the perfect picture of the Christian, and the canvas is painted with the colors of the winged things that appear on the fifth day of Creation. What is the picture? Here it is: the true believer in the Lord Jesus is characterized by the presence in his life of the Holy Spirit, and that means sweetness and light. The bitterness of the flesh is done away and forgotten in His coming, and as the song of the cooing dove delights the heart of every hearer, our song of praise of Him who is the Creator and the Saviour as well, should turn all men's hearts to Him. This is the message of the winged things, and the purpose of their creation, and again the record is completely in accord with the words of our Lord: "If ye had believed Moses ye would believe Me. for Moses wrote of Me."

Zoology and the Lamb of God

Genesis Chapter One:

24. And God said, Let the earth bring forth the living creature after his kind, cattle, and creeping thing, and beast of the earth after his kind: and it was so.

25. And God made the beast of the earth after his kind, and cattle after their kind, and everything that creepeth upon the earth after his kind: and God saw that *it was* good.

CHAPTER TEN

Zoology and the Lamb of God

THE first five days of this week of God's labor were planned to furnish the earth with everything essential to man's welfare. When God crowned His creative activity with the appearance of mankind, this new lord of the universe did not move into an empty habitation. We must bear in mind that while the prologue to this creative week states that the earth *had become* empty, unfurnished and chaotic, God had now been busy in these six marvelous days assembling new furniture.

When this sixth day closes, we see that the house is now completely furnished with all that the tenant will need. Not only does the work of this day complete the furniture, but it marks the creation of the tenant as well! It becomes humorously apparent that earthly landlords are thus under a handicap. There would be no depression if a human being had power to build an apartment house, to create the furniture, and could then call into being a tenant to occupy this domicile and pay rent for the span of his natural life. This, alas, is not possible, and perhaps it is well that it is so. There would be no depression, but there would shortly be an overproduction as greedy human landlords filled the earth with more life than it could support.

Textual observations are necessary in introducing the work of the sixth day. The phrase "Let the earth bring forth" does not imply creative forces in the soil or in any of the physical elements. The ninety-two elements have been in existence from the first verse of Genesis, "In the beginning God created" . . . them. They had certainly been filling the sphere for the past five days of this week, but no life had emerged from them.

We have dealt casually in a previous chapter with the fallacy of the theory of spontaneous generation, and this day accentuates the impossibility of life arising by natural forces. The intelligent biologist who thinks his way through without diversion from known fact cannot but be amused at the childlike, ingenuous comments of the sponsors of this theory. A typical example is from the pen of Dr. Edwin O. Jordan in the famous symposium published by sixteen university professors of Chicago, bearing the imposing title, "The Nature of the World and of Man." We quote this paragraph in full:

"While there is little or no cause to believe that spontaneous generation is occurring at the present day, it is reasonable to suppose that some form of microscopic life developed out of inorganic matter at some previous period in the world's history. The continuity of development which is so striking a feature of the life-record found in fossil rocks may thus be seen to extend back to include the orderly and progressive development of the organic out of the inorganic. It is a remarkable possibility to contemplate—but no more remarkable than the known facts about the marvelous growth of crystals and the still more wonderful transmutation of one element into another, radium into helium, thorium into lead. We naturally have no direct evidence about the origin of bacteria on the earth, but it is quite in line with all of our other knowledge of life development to suppose that at some time in some way some form of microscopic life developed out of highly organized, but up to that time, inorganic matter."

The remarkable inaccuracy of this citation is attested by the very life-record found in fossil-bearing rocks that is cited by the author of this striking paragraph. The plain fact of paleontology is that there is no continuity of development from species to species and from genus to genus. The known growth of crystals and the transformation of one element into another are not analogous to the transmutation of one biological species into a subsequent and higher species. Nor is there anything in nature that is comparable to the miracle of sentient life. No growth, no reproduction, no generation and no quickening of inorganic matter has ever been demonstrated in any field of science whatever. When the author states that, "it is quite in line with all of our other knowledge of life development to suppose that at some time in some way some form of microscopic life developed out of highly organized, but up to that time, inorganic matter," he either ignores all of the known facts of biology or for the purpose of special pleading disregards this considerable body of knowledge. The basic law of biology is that life comes only from living ancestry. The *origin* of life in biology absolutely demands a creative act as far as our present scientific knowledge is concerned.

The only word of truth in this entire paragraph is the statement that there is little or no cause to believe that spontaneous generation is occurring at this present time. This school of unscientific "die-hards," who are eternally striving to explain the origin of life apart from creation, have evolved the idea that spontaneous generation was once possible because of the heat of the cooling earth. So they say life began in a puddle of hot water. This is an ingenious attempt to evade the issue. It would be far more truthful to say that man has been in hot water ever since his appearance on the face of the earth, but he began in Eden's garden.

The Hebrew phrase translated in the English version by the phrase, "creeping things," embraces the entire order of reptilia. Everything of a serpent nature that the earth contains emerged from the crucible of creation in the magnificent work of this day.

We note also the amazing scientific accuracy with which this text differentiates between the beast of the field and the cattle. The Hebrew word that is here translated "beast of the field" is "cheva," while the "cattle" are "behemah." Certainly there is scientific accuracy in the accompanying phrase of reproduction "after its own kind."

This is the finest summary of the law of Mendel that ever has been made, even though it appeared ages before Mendel's law was formulated. There is no exception in modern biology to this ancient dictum of Moses, and, as far as the records of paleontology are concerned, there has never been an exception to this fiat. Indeed, it is one of the beneficial graces of Providence that it is so. Without this law rigidly enforced, the earth in one generation would be peopled with such abominable monstrosities as to render life unsupportable for intelligent beings. There are some weird and remarkable creatures known to man which are more or less harmless because they keep to their natural sphere. It would be fascinating to exercise our imagination and contemplate a world where this law of biology was not enforced.

If the eagle could mate with the leopard, producing a predatory, feline hybrid with wings, how unhappy would be the lot of the dwellers in the land where that particular monstrosity was common. If the rattlesnake could cross with the bird, producing a venomous hybrid that would smite from the air, cast iron umbrellas would quickly come into vogue. Imagine the hybrid that would result if the crocodile mated with the elephant, or the tiger with the shark. Weird indeed would be the dilemma of humanity if creation forgot the commands of the careful Creator when He said, each "after its own kind."

Keeping these simple textual notes in mind, we pass on to the consideration of the paragraph of Genesis that we quoted at the beginning of this chapter.

The creation of cattle is a specific evidence of God's provision for man. In all of the amazing furniture of this earth, devised to make life easy for man, there is nothing that can compare with the creatures that Moses calls cattle. They are the best and most patient servants of mankind.

Some of them furnish him with clothing.

Some of them furnish man with food.

Some provide him with labor; and there are others that provide him with all three.

One of the commonest examples of the many varieties of cattle that serve man is found in the humble creature called the sheep. This gentle and harmless creature that has so entranced the poet and Psalmist alike, is found as far back in history as the record of man goes. Sheep have always been the companion of man, and one of his chief sources of subsistence. In fact, the Hyksos kings of ancient Egypt were called the "Shepherd Kings" because of the extent of their flocks and herds. The Hyksos dynasty was in Egypt, but these rulers were Semites. The Egyptians despised herdsmen, and we have here an historical fact that illuminates the reception that Israel received when Joseph brought his brothers into Egypt.

We remember the shrewdness of his advice to his brethren, when he urged them to tell the Pharaoh that they were herdsmen. There was no competition among the Egyptians for the job of tending the flocks of Pharaoh. Coming into Egypt as immigrants, their property depleted by the seven years of famine, Joseph's brothers needed to make a new start in life. When the Pharaoh asked their occupation they simply replied, "We be herdsmen," and they had a lifelong job!

Pastoral Israel was connected with sheep from the time their race began. It is a matter of record that the greatest king Israel ever saw was a man whom God took from the sheepcote, and made king of the nation.

Sheep have a universal ministry for the welfare of man. They provide us with clothing. The wool is clipped from their bodies and woven into garments to keep man warm. It is not necessary that one should have lived on the Western plains and Southern ranges, to know that the cow-puncher hates a sheep with a bitter and implacable enmity. To call a self-respecting cowboy a sheep-herder, is to invite battle that is instant. The very smell of a sheep unsettles a cowboy's appetite and leaves him disgruntled for the rest of the day. Yet in our

experiences on the range, we have noticed that every cowboy
who faces the wintry blasts in the necessity of his rigorous
calling, clothes himself in a sheepskin jacket! Though he may
despise the animal in life, he must accept its protection and
its care to help him survive the rigors of his occupation. There
is an element of humor in this situation.

They provide us with medicine. In the biological labora-
tories where vaccines and serums are produced for the use of
suffering mankind, the sheep is one of the commonest animals
used in this ministry.

Even in death their work does not close, as we use their
skin for leather. Their ministry does not end with that, for
after a sheep has served man faithfully all of its natural life,
when it finally dies of old age, we buy it over the counter of
the butcher shop as lamb chops, or shoulder of spring lamb!

In Scripture as well as in history the sheep is prominent.
In revelation they first enter the record when Abel is received by God because he offers a lamb in sacrifice. The sheep
reaches the crest of Scriptural prominence in Old Testament
ages, in the twelfth chapter of Exodus. Here the blood of the
paschal lamb is recognized by God as a means of refuge from
death and disaster, so we still sing that ancient refrain, "When
I, the Lord, shall see the blood, I will pass over you." The
record of the lamb in revelation progresses from glory to glory
until John meets Jesus by the banks of Jordan and says, "Behold the Lamb of God, which taketh away the sin of the
world." To complete the picture the triumphant Son of God
is called "The Lamb" twenty-six times in the last book of the
Bible where John shows him enshrined in heaven.

We are thus reminded that the contributions of the sheep
to the welfare of man have been not only physical, but spiritual as well. They appear in all the ages before Christ as the
means of man's salvation.

We have frequently been asked why God calls us His sheep.
To this we can only reply, "We do not know." It may be,

however, because sheep are the stupidest creatures known in the world of zoology. They always lose their way. In the amazing aggregation of entertainment and instruction that modern man calls the circus, we have seen almost every known animal perform, but we have never seen a trained sheep. A dog or cat, all the farm animals, and everything that can be caught in traps, may be taught to perform for the amusement of man with the apparent exception of the sheep. Perhaps the Lord God, considering the stupidity of the human family, just shook His head and said, "We will call them sheep."

Sheep are stupid and cannot find their way without a guide. You couldn't lose a horse; he always knows his way home. Many times in the Western mountains we have been hopelessly lost, but were always able to return to the starting place by turning the horse loose and letting him find his own way. The sagacity of the horse is proverbial. We remember that in the days of our youth we used to drive a milk wagon; the horse knew every customer on the route. From the time we set out from the dairy until the time we returned to the barn, we never touched the reins to guide that intelligent animal. He stopped at the right places, and turned at the right corners, and knew that route better than we did. Indeed, we told the superintendent of the dairy that if the horse knew which customer received a pint and which one got a quart, he wouldn't need a driver.

It is difficult to lose a dog. Take him many miles from home and turn him loose, and later, sometimes with the pads of his feet worn to the quick, he will come limping home.

It used to be the custom, when people moved from one house to another, to put lard on the paws of the cat. This intelligent animal wouldn't walk with greasy feet, and by the time she had the lard licked off she had become accustomed to the new home, and was willing to stay. Without some such stratagem, the cat would inevitably return.

Even a cow, not generally noted for brains and wisdom,

will come down the lane to the pasture bars at eventide, waiting for the gate to be opened that she may come home.

But take a sheep half way from the barn to the haystack and turn it loose, and it is hopelessly lost and can't find its way back.

Though there be pasture within easy reach, the sheep is apparently incapable of finding it for itself. It must have a guide. So God, looking at stupid, lost humanity, said, "All they like sheep have gone astray."

Sheep are among the dirtiest animals associated with man. The natural tendency of wool in its raw and wild state is to pick up any defilement with which it comes into contact. There is a very unpleasant odor that is natural to the sheep, and this has been one of the chief reasons for the dislike engendered in the cowboy's breast.

Mud dries on the pelt of the sheep in the most bedraggled patterns imaginable. The adherence of the mud is persistent. No matter how dry it may become, it does not seem to powder and fall away. Above all creatures that are associated with the life of man, the sheep is unquestionably the dirtiest. The poet who sings the praise of the snow-white sheep rarely sees them in their typical natural conditions, journeying together in great flocks. The dust of their passage adheres to their person until they become as brown as the terrain over which they travel.

Of all the creatures in the world, the sheep has the greatest need of cleansing. So God looked at pitiable humanity, foul and unclean, bearing the marks of their passage through centuries of sin, and said, "We will call them sheep."

That we are the sheep of God is at least logical, in that the sheep is one of the few animals totally incapable of self-cleansing. We have all seen the domesticated cat sit down after a meal and carefully make her toilet. The genus homo is supposed to be the most intelligent creature in the realm of biology; nevertheless, kittens are born with instinctive knowledge that the male juvenile of the human family does not possess. We refer to the apparent ability in self-cleansing that enables a cat to wash her own neck and ears without instructions from her mother. With a final pat, she combs out her whiskers and has made herself clean and neat. On innumerable occasions we have seen the dog on the farm quietly slip into a flowing stream and swim about, evidently for the sole purpose of taking a bath. Even the despised outcast of the animal kingdom, called the rat, can be seen, in moments of relaxation, cleansing his person. But the dirtier a sheep gets, the more helpless it becomes. In this respect it seems to be below the hog. Many times we have seen a shoat rubbing its person against the lower railing of the fence, scratching off the caked mud — but a sheep, never. So God looked at poor faulty humanity and said, "If We don't clean them, they'll never be cleansed. We will call them Our sheep."

Sheep are among the most tender of creatures, always suffering hurt and pain. We have skinned the carcasses of many of them, but we have never seen a sheep pelt that was unscarred or unbruised. They spend half their days bleating because of physical distress, and the rest of their time bumping into something else to hurt themselves again. Without natural joy because of the tenderness of their constitution, they become the perfect type of man.

They are dependent, and must always be provided for. Indeed, their only alluring quality is their very helplessness. We have seen the very roughest of Mexican shepherds stop and take into their comforting arms tired lambs that could no longer keep the pace of the flock. So He takes us to His bosom, as the shepherd cradles his lambs, moved by our very need and helpless estate, declares us to be His sheep, and appoints Himself our shepherd.

As closely associated with the life of man as are the sheep, we find the vast company of bovine servants. Like sheep, the cows are planned, designed, and formed to be of service to man. From the time of our infancy to the exit of this life through the door of old age, we are surrounded by the beneficence provided by the cow. She makes her primary contributions to us in the gift of the life-giving fluid we have named milk. It is a rare thing, indeed, to find a human being who cannot subsist on milk. We are acquainted with many scores of people who lived one whole year on nothing but cow's milk, and more than doubled their weight in that time. This, of course, applies to the first year that they have graced this earth.

Some time ago an eminent manufacturer of automobiles made a criticism of the cow. We could understand this criticism if it were directed at the horse, but since a cow is not in competition with the tractor, the insult seems to be gratuitous! The comment was that the cow is an inefficient machine. For the amount of fodder she consumes, we receive something less than fourteen per cent in the form of butterfat and milk. The statement was made that in a modern laboratory, by a process of synthesis, ninety per cent of this same material could be reduced to artificial milk. We do not question the accuracy of this statement, as we realize that creative chemistry today can produce this substance artificially.

Synthetic milk, when seen in the test tube, responds to every test that the cow's contribution would meet. There is, however, a vital difference. A calf or a baby, fed upon artificial milk, would be content, and never feel a pang of hunger, but within ninety days would die of starvation. Inefficient as the cow may be, she possesses a secret unknown to modern science, in that she has within herself the mystery of putting the element that is life into her contribution for man's welfare. Better fourteen per cent returns that spell life than ninety per cent that lead to death! We cannot take the space or time to exhaust consideration of the contribution of the cow; but let us consider that from the milk we receive cream, which is useful in many different forms. From the coffee cup to the confectioner's freezer, we have centered much of our enjoyment around this yellow substance found only on the top of the cow's milk. From this same element of milk we receive cheese and butter.

Even in the hour of its death, the service of the cow continues, for having fed us multiplied years with these generous contributions, when she reaches a timely end, she then becomes beef to please the gourmand's palate. Stripping her body of her natural covering, we convert it to the leather of a thousand uses. Not content to rest the case there, we grind her bones into phosphates to put into the fertilizer to spread upon our fields to grow more hay to feed more cows, whose bones we will grind to use as fertilizer to put in the ground to raise more hay for more cows that come after her.

The crowning contribution, after the death of this generous creature, is the delightful confection that greets most children at Sunday evening tea — from the hoofs and horns of the cow — the "nervous" dessert, jello. When we consider the manifold uses, as well as these more personal contributions, we must come to the conclusion that the cow was designed as a beneficent creature to be the servant of man. So patient and generous are these animals, that we have often seen them hooked to the plow or harrow providing man with labor as well as food. They will bear the cold of Labrador or the heat of Peru with equal facility, and are thus able to accompany man in his migration. The cow has aided man as much as the horse. Nations have been subdued and depopulated by warriors mounted upon cavalry steeds. These conquests, that in some cases decimated the citizens of a country, were possible with the aid of a horse. When those lands that had thus suffered were finally restored to normal population, however, it was partly through the beneficent ministry of the cow.

These ruminating creatures are equipped with a marvelous apparatus which testifies to the certainty of design in very positive terms. It occasionally causes surprise when we inform some people that the cow is equipped with four stomachs. One evening we said this to a company of youngsters, and one small boy on the front seat laughed with very evident enjoyment. We stopped to ask the cause of his merriment and he said, "I am glad I am not a cow. Last night I had a stomach ache, and one was enough."

When a cow crops her fodder, she hastily and imperfectly chews this food, and swallows it into stomach number one. Whenever she drinks any fluid, that goes directly into stomach number two. The fodder in stomach number one, by peristaltic action, is rolled into small balls, and passed over into number two, where it is saturated with the fluid, and left until the cow has leisure to chew. By a simple contraction of a muscular apparatus, she regurgitates these balls of fodder from stomach number two back into her mouth, where they are thoroughly masticated. When the fodder is swallowed the second time, thoroughly masticated, it goes into stomach number three. There it is refined and passed on to stomach number four, where the process of digestion continues until it is converted into chyle. In this fluid form the food passes out of stomach number four into the blood stream of the mammal as is the custom in all mammalian digestion.

Although we have often studied the anatomy of the cow, we have never found a signpost, highway marker, traffic cop, or directing agency; but we never saw a cow's food that has lost its way. Into the right stomach it goes, and out again, never becoming confused in its passage.

This is even more remarkable when we consider the peculiar actions of the calf. Its processes of digestion are worthy of a special note. Although the calf is born with four stomachs, at first it uses only one for food. When it drinks water, that fluid goes into stomach number two, as in the case of the adult cow, but when the calf drinks milk, this milk makes a detour and takes a short cut directly into stomach number four. The purpose of the first three stomachs is to reduce the solid food to a fluid state. The milk, being in this condition primarily, disdains the aid of the first three, and seeks at once that stomach which is prepared to receive it. But, without instructions from the farmer or the cow, the first mouthful of solid food the young calf learns to eat, heads straight for stomach number one, and begins this process of journeying from stomach to stomach. This special equipment has prepared the cow to ruminate, migrate, and masticate. In all the world of nature, the beneficent Creator has given us no finer evidence of His provision and care for man in furnishing this globe than in this creature that is the cow.

One of the most outstanding evidences of design in creation is the provision God has made for the desert dweller, in the creature called the camel. Those weird monstrosities would seem to be a holdover of the Pleistocene period, if it were not for the evidence of design they bear in their structure. If you never saw a camel, and somebody tried to describe to you this odd-looking animal, you would say, "There is no such animal."

When the late Theodore Roosevelt was engaged in an expedition to Africa, it is humorously told that his son, Kermit, discovered an odd-looking bird unknown to many in those parts. Describing this bird to his father, who was an eminent ornithologist, Kermit asked for the name of the bird. After listening to a painstaking description of the bird, the colonel said, "There is no such bird." Kermit went back the next day to this roost with his powerful binoculars and studied the bird again. This time he made some sketches, and returned to describe the bird to his father. Mr. Roosevelt listened patiently and then said, "There is no such bird." The Roosevelt disposition was so strong in Kermit that he returned the third night armed with a gun. When the bird hit the roost, the gun cracked and the bird hit the ground. Picking the bird up in triumph, he laid it down before his father, and said, "Now, what kind of bird is that?" Solemnly and with great interest, Mr. Roosevelt examined the bird, point by point. At last, apparently satisfied, he laid it down and said, "You see, son, I was right; there is no such bird."

We feel that way whenever we see a camel. We look at his amazing, pendulous lip, the large articulation of its legs, the humps on its back, its . . . . tail, and the odd appearance of its coat; then we shake our heads and say, "There is no such animal."

It was characteristic of the keen humor of the Lord Jesus that when He desired to arouse the laughter of the great crowds against the prejudices of the Pharisee, He used this beast. His indictment, "You strain out the gnat and swallow the camel", must have been received by the Oriental company with gales of laughter. Their keen imagination would get busy at once. Of all the creatures on earth, the ungainly camel would be hardest to swallow. If you started with the head, those hind legs would stick out, kicking and squirming, and they would be the last things to disappear from sight. If you tried to swallow him the other way around, that long neck would be left protuding from the mouth of the masticator, with the blubbering lips and the goggling eyes of the sad looking beast bidding a final farewell! Since the Oriental sense of humor is quick to frame itself with imageries, this comical situation would appeal to that sense of humor at once. Yet we have heard some maintain that Jesus never manifested a sense of humor.

Monstrous and weird as the camel is, however, it is God's gift to the desert dweller. Its foot is designed for traction in sand. It is the perfect type of cord tire. One summer when we were returning from an expedition in the Southeastern desert, we met a man, unlearned in the ways of sandy wastes, who was in serious trouble. Thinking that travel on the unbroken sand would be smoother than the bumpy desert highway, he had left the road and had become embedded in the treacherous terrain. In an attempt to loose himself he had mounted his skid chains, and had dug himself in to the hub caps. We had not sufficient rope or chains to reach him from the highway, and knew better than to leave the safety of solid footing.

We walked out to this disconsolate and stranded traveler, and offered our aid. It was eagerly accepted. Upon the man's promise to do what we said, with the assurance that we would extricate him from his trouble, he seated himself beneath the wheel ready to start the motor, while we went around and let the air out of all four tires. In consternation and surprise, he said just once, "Are you sure this is going to work?" Upon our positive affirmation, he merely grunted, and allowed us to proceed.

When we had exhausted the air in his tires, he turned on the motor, and with three of us shoving from the rear, he worked the car out from the crust of ashen sand to the safety of the highway. The last we saw of him as we drove down the road, he was standing with a tire pump in his hand, and a happy look on his face. When seasoned desert travelers are stuck in treacherous footing, they generally know enough to emulate the camel, and walk out on padded feet!

If God did not thus create him, why is it that this one creature is fitted to be the servant of man in the desert, and is by nature adapted to that desert? The strange coriaceous pads on the anatomy of the camel mark him as designed to be a burden bearer. His whole body is planned for desert existence.

The second stomach of the camel is a reservoir in which he stores the precious fluid he needs for drink. Though days succeed each other in intolerable heat, he calmly sips the necessary moisture from his second stomach to keep him refreshed and strengthened. In a land where food is almost unknown, the camel carries his own pantry on his back. A certain percentage of all food eaten by the camel is in excess of his daily need. This extra energy, in the form of fat, is stored in the humps of the camel. If he is forced to go day after day without food, he subsists upon the food thus preserved. After days of such fasting, the skin hangs flaccid and loose, and the humps disappear. These benevolent equipments enable him to travel day after day without food and water in a land where both are scarce.

Can any deny in the face of this, that the camel is God's gift to the desert dweller? The milk of the camel is used by these nomadic people as we use the milk of the cow. We would not advise our readers to attempt to eat camel cheese, unless they were suffering from severe colds in their heads. It is a delicacy only to those who are accustomed to it from their childhood, and have had their sensibilities thus blunted. The hair of the camel is woven into cloth and made into tents to shelter this animal's owner from the inclemency of the weather. The dried dung of the camel is the only fuel that some deserts possess. With a final contribution of meat for the diner's table, the camel serves the desert dweller in such an amazing and perfect fashion that we can but conclude that God created this creature to be the servant of man.

Time and space will not permit us to more than mention the horse, the foremost burden bearer of man, a creature of the utmost grace, symmetry, and perfected beauty. His strength mitigated by affection for man, he has contributed greatly by his speed and docility to man's conquest of the earth. The patient and lowly ox, the frolicking dog, and the animals innumerable, associated in the domestic life of man, are all among God's greatest gifts to our welfare and convenience.

Although Moses clearly distinguishes between those which are the cattle and those which are the beasts of the field, we must not conclude that the latter are valueless to man. But before we comment upon the usefulness of the wild beasts let us note how amazing it is that this first commentator on the world of zoology should so carefully distinguish between these two separated orders of life. What a world of suggestion we find in that phrase, "The cattle *and* the beasts of the field."

Of what use would be the qualities of a sheep if it possessed the disposition of a jackal? Of what use would the cow be to the farmer if it had the disposition of a lion? Suppose some farmer went out in the early darkness of a winter morning with his milk stool in one hand and his lantern in his other to garner the contributions of the cow. Suddenly possessed with the disposition of a lion, the cow, hearing the approach of the farmer, tears loose from her tether. With several growls and gnashing of teeth, she climbs to the nethermost rafter of the barn, and there, crouching with her tail lashing her flanks, she launches herself like a thunderbolt on the farmer!

Of what benefit to man would the quality of the horse prove to be if the horse were as blood-thirsty as the tiger? There is no natural reason why these animals should so differ. The supernatural reason is that God created them that way. The beasts of the field were evidently not planned by Providence as servants of the farmer.

If the quadrumanes would pick cotton they would displace the darkies of the South in one year's time. If a herd of baboons could be taught to lie on their backs between two rows of cotton and pick the fleecy clusters with all four feet, the harvesting would be complete in a day. The trouble is, however, such labor is entirely against their nature. Turn these apes loose in a field of cotton, and they would wreck it hopelessly in an hour. The leopard would be a valuable adjunct to the animals on the farm if he would restrict himself to pest control. This proposition is not feasible, however, as this gorgeous cat would eat rats one day and the baby the next!

It is evident, however, as we study this world of nature, that even the wildest beast of the field has its practical use for men. One of the most inexcusable ignorances to our thinking minds in the twentieth century, is man's hatred for snakes. We can understand this disposition to fear and dread the poison variety, but this hatred extends to the most harmless and truly beneficial. Observing the diet of the ordinary gopher or bull snake, we compute their value to the farmer as being within the range of two hundred and fifty dollars a year up to much more, depending upon their size. The rodents form the natural diet of these harmless reptiles. These rodents would consume crops to that value every twelve months if the snakes did not keep them subdued. Some day when these gentle and friendly creatures are truly understood, they will be protected by law, as are the singing birds.

They also have the evidence of special creation in their structural design. Many of them live entirely upon the smaller rodents that are such a pest to agriculture; eating animals in many cases that are far larger in diameter than the diner itself! Thus they are equipped with four jaws that all disarticulate at the will of their possessor, so they may stretch their mouths to unbelievable widths to accommodate their small structure to the enormous meal. Then crawling over and around the prey, they slowly engulf the rodent, sometimes taking many minutes, and often even hours, to accomplish this act of swallowing.

During all this time the trachea is constricted by the width of the passing food and the snake would suffocate if it did not have a secondary breathing apparatus to function during this time. Here, then, is creation, indeed! If the theory of organic evolution is true, and the organs of various animals were all produced in response to a need, then the first snake would have suffocated while this organ was being developed. But if the first snake appeared with this special equipment for a peculiar need, then that is creation; to which fact the entire animal kingdom bears an unswerving record.

The entire animal world also seems to assent to the record that Moses here contends for; that is, they were all created to serve man in some way. The balance of Nature is a marvelous thing, and it is never safe for man to interfere with this arrangement. Even the creatures that we list as pests are useful in the divine economy, and have their humble place in fitting this earth for our enjoyment. We will illustrate this by the record of that farming community in our own state, where a

certain influential man saw a coyote capture one of his prize
hens one evening. He started a crusade to have a bounty put
on the head of this animal to exterminate it. The campaign
succeeded; the coyotes were wiped out of the county; and then
the jack-rabbits got so thick in four years that the farmers had
to spend an aggregate fortune to build rabbit-proof fences to
save some of their crops. They would now pay fifty dollars
apiece to get their coyotes back!

It would weary the reader and occupy a book the size of the
Encyclopedia Britannica if we were actually to exhaust the
evidences of intelligence imparted to the animals of the field,
as they manifest this in their daily lives. This is, in the final
analysis, the greatest argument for creation the natural world
affords the philosophical student. When creatures so low in
the scale of life, that they are classed as "the lower animals,"
manifest a skill in building that man cannot equal; when the
humblest of the moving things act in exact fellowship with the
profoundest laws of nature, it is evident to the careful thinker
that some higher source of knowledge is being met with in
their conduct.

No man has ever attained the engineering skill of the lowly
beaver. All the human beings in the world working together,
could never duplicate the marvel of the home built by the
living bodies of the army ants. No one of the trained army of
human flyers can ever approach to the zenith attained by the
Atta queen in her mating flight. These creatures of God's
handiwork are the witnesses to the truth of Moses, and they
are prepared to take the stand day and night and testify to the
inspiration of these words we have set ourselves to study.

The animal creation, that appears as the first work of the
Sixth Day, preaches the Gospel of the Grace of the Son of God
with ceaseless and mighty eloquence. From the first book of
the Bible to, and through, the last, they are types of the work
of redemption that Jesus wrought when He died in our stead
on Calvary. Although the animals of the sacrifice are those

that appear in the life and community interest of man, the creatures of the wild also have their part in the imagery and foreshadowing of the manner by which salvation would come forth. The animals of the Bible are not only remarkably numerous, but they are among the best preachers in its pages.

We commonly use the phrase, "dumb as an ox," but the ox is dignified by becoming the type of the Lord Jesus, ages before He comes. Indeed, this creature is mentioned in the sacred text almost a hundred and fifty times. It portrays the person of the Messiah, in that He becomes the humble, patient, and enduring servant of his fellows, and their Saviour as well; for the ox was one of the chief animals of the sacrifice. It was especially used in the peace offering. Thus, by shedding his blood, the ox pointed the human race to Him who came to speak to them that were afar off.

Who among us does not remember that the scapegoat so well portrayed the work of the Redeemer through the ages that the hungry hearts of believing men were longing for His appearing. This animal had the dual role to enact; he died for the sins of the people, and he bore them away out of the land of remembrance.

If you have not read this chapter recently, turn again to the sixteenth of Leviticus, and read again the strange account of this ceremony of atonement. When the day came that the High Priest was to enter into the Holy Place where God would meet him for the redemption of the people, he was to take a young bullock, sacrifice it for his own sins and then put on the holy garments of linen. Thus covered by blood and attired in the garments of righteousness, he was to take two goats by lot. On one, which the lot designated, the sins of the people were typically placed, and, bearing their sins on himself, this goat was driven forth into the wilderness. The other was slain, and his blood placed before the altar, as was the custom with most of the sacrifices.

The goat that was driven forth to an uninhabited land was called "the scapegoat." Thus we see the picture of the two-fold work of Jesus: He died for our sins, in truth, but He also lived to bear them away to the Land of God's Forgetting; for we have the promise of Our Father that when our sins are on the Saviour, God will remember them no more. There are three references to this type of the goat in the New Testament, all of them directly applied by the writers to the work of our Lord. The first one is in John one, twenty-nine, where the Baptist cries, "Behold the Lamb of God, which *taketh away* the sin of the world." This phrase "taketh away" is a direct reference to the type of the scapegoat, that did bear the sins of the people to the far-away. The second reference to this beautiful ceremony is in Hebrews nine, twenty-eight. Here the inspired Apostle who penned these words at the dictation of the Holy Ghost, refers to this same event when he writes: "So Christ was once offered *to bear the sins of many*." He, in His own body, not only bore our sins on Calvary's tree, but also bore our sins away, to be forgotten forever. Thus he fulfills the type of the *two* goats—the one that was slain and the one that became the sin-bearer. The final reference to this is in the first epistle of John, second chapter and second verse. When the writer states, "and He is the *propitiation* for our sins," he makes reference to this rite that all Israel knew so well in the ceremony of the scapegoat.

How quaint to recall that in our modern English slang, this very fact is so often observed!

"What?" you will say, "The Gospel in slang?"

Indeed, yes.

When the innocent is willing to suffer for the guilty, how often we hear such an one say, "Well, I didn't do it, *but I'll be the goat.*"

We hear the unwilling victim of another's wrongdoing exclaim, "Here, now, you can't make me the goat!"

The very word scapegoat, so common in our modern speech, is used to define the experience of one that is made to suffer for the sins of some other. This ceremony, given to Israel in anticipation of the coming of the divine Sin-bearer, has thus worked its way into the imagery and remembrance of the modern world, until we can never forget the picture.

Prominent among the animals of Scripture, the red heifer stands as the type of the believer's cleansing. In the nineteenth chapter of Numbers the record of this method of cleansing the sinner is given to God's people as part of the marvelous dramatized ceremonies of the ancient covenant. To impress upon His people the iniquitous nature of sin and disobedience, all who may have violated the code of God were declared by the law to be unclean. This implied actual separation for them, and no man or woman who was clean in the sight of God could have fellowship with the unclean, until the latter had become clean again. The heinousness of sin was further impressed on the people in the picture of the sacrifice provided for this particular ceremony. It must be a red heifer, without spot or blemish, and one that had never known the yoke of service to man. When slain in accordance with the specific instructions of the Lord, this sacrifice provided a manner by which the guilty one could be made clean.

All this symbolized the efficacy of the redemption that is in Christ Jesus, as His salvation is not simply to *save* the sinner, but also to keep him saved! The one reference in the New Testament to this act seems to be in Hebrews thirteen, eleven and twelve. The paragraph refers to the fact that the bodies of the beasts that were sacrificed were "burned without the camp." As the nineteenth chapter of Numbers tells in the third verse that this was specifically done in the case of the red heifer, it seems clear that the reference following: "Wherefore Jesus also, that He might sanctify the people with His own blood, suffered without the gate," refers to this picture of the Old Testament.

The ram was the animal that characteristically portrayed the sinner's substitute. This is set forth clearly in the notable incident of the twenty-second chapter of Genesis. Abraham, "the man who believed God," had come to a place of testing that few men could ever face. To prove his love and devotion, he had been asked to sacrifice his only son on the altar, and thus demonstrate that he loved his God above every other thing. With a faith that was magnificent in its calm certainty, he hastened to obey.

We are generally so lost in admiration of Abraham for this demonstration of faith that we fail to recognize another faith equally as great. This is the fact that Isaac, the son to be sacrificed, *was willing to die,* if that should prove to be the will of his father, and the will of his father's God! For ages we have been picturing the "lad," Isaac, as a tender youngster of immature years, but such is not the case. As nearly as can be worked out in the chronology of the events, he must have been about thirty years of age. This would make Abraham about one hundred and thirty years old; and certainly no man of that age could have bound and sacrificed a hale young man of thirty, if the stronger one had not been willing! Thus we are reminded again, that even though "God so loved the world, that He gave His only begotten Son," the Son was equally willing to be given!

We hear again, across the sweep of the ages, the calm reply of Abraham, when Isaac asked about the animal for the sacrifice: "God will Himself provide the offering!" And sure enough; there was *the ram,* waiting to be the sinner's substitute. Thus we see again this animal of humble origin, used by God in the Old Testament to point us to the One Who would in time bear the sins of man, and become the sinner's substitute for all ages.

We have already referred to the sheep, patient unto death, led as a lamb to the slaughter, dumb before her shearers, as the perfect type of the Saviour. The Oriental mind, visualizing everything in the language of pictures, had thus been prepared for the advent of Him Who was to become the means of salvation. Through all the ages some of them had waited for His appearing, made ready by these symbolical portrayals of redemption through the animals of the Sixth Day.

These animals, acceptable for sacrifice and atonement, were all domestic creatures, with one outstanding exception. It was thus apparent that only that which had a community interest in the life of man could avail him in the ordinances of forgiveness; which again explains how and why God's Son took upon Himself the flesh of a man. By the community interest of thirty-three years of human living, Jesus so identified Himself with the affairs of perishing humanity, that He became logically able to save from this perishing condition those who were willing.

The one exception, referred to in the foregoing paragraph, was the serpent. The only creature of the wild, as far as we can trace the history of these events, that ever became a type of Jesus was the serpent in the wilderness. The account, as given in the twenty-first chapter of Numbers, is very familiar to all Bible students, so we shall merely recapitulate the event in a few words, by way of reminder.

Murmuring against God and the leader He had given (which same was a favorite occupation among the Children of Israel!), the horde entered the Wilderness of Zin. There, to punish them for their murmuring, the Lord sent a plague upon them in the form of "fiery serpents." These reptiles were common vipers, about eighteen inches long, that infested the region, but that appeared in uncommon numbers at that place and time. It seems to be the method of God in most cases, to use just what is at hand but in greater numbers and divinely guided to the purpose He desires to accomplish. So with these small vipers. They were a coppery red, and so deadly that there was no cure known that was efficacious in the case of the man bitten by them. Death was inevitable.

When people suffer, they think; and so with the Israelites. Coming to Moses, the priest and leader, they cried out, "We have sinned! Entreat God for us, that this plague may pass away." As was ever the custom of this man Moses, he exercised his priestly function and sought of God a remedy for the suffering of the people. True to His eternal purpose, the Lord God was more than willing to treat with repentant sinners, and prescribed the strangest cure for snake bite the earth has ever seen.

His instructions to Moses were simple. "Make an image of the serpent *in brass*, erect it on a pole in the center of camp; and it shall come to pass that when a man is bitten by the fiery serpent, if he will look to the brazen serpent he will live, and not die!" We do not suppose Moses knew *how* God would work this miracle, but he certainly knew *why*. In the picture-language of that day, the serpent stood as the type of sin, and brass as the picture of Judgment. So when Moses erected the brazen serpent, it spoke to all there in a language that they could thoroughly comprehend, and told the tale of sin judged, and forgiveness accorded.

So centuries later, Jesus Christ used this record as the basis of His great ministry, when He said, "As Moses lifted up the serpent in the wilderness, even so must the Son of Man be lifted up: that whosoever believeth in Him should not perish, but have eternal life." And again He refers to this event when He says, "And I, if I be lifted up, will draw all men unto Me." John states that thus He described the death He was to die. And so, on the authority of the New Testament, we accept the serpent of the wilderness experience as a type of Jesus, and note this one creature of the wild that enters into the record of atonement.

At the very beginning of these meditations, we announced a two-fold purpose. First, we said we would look for the evidences of design in Creation which would vindicate the claims of the true believers that Moses was inspired by the Holy

Spirit in the writing of this record; and, secondly, that he wrote of Jesus in all his words and revelation. *Truly we have accomplished this two-fold purpose in the work of this day.* The animal creation testifies to the truth and supernatural source of the words of Moses; and his words point us again and again to *"The Lamb of God, which taketh away the sin of the World."*

The Creation of Adam

Genesis Chapter One:

26.   And God said, Let us make man in our image, after our likeness: and let them have dominion over the fish of the sea, and over the fowl of the air, and over the cattle, and over all the earth, and over every creeping thing that creepeth upon the earth.

27.   And so God created man in his *own* image, in the image of God created he him; male and female created he them.

28.   And God blessed them, and God said unto them, Be fruitful, and multiply, and replenish the earth, and subdue it: and have dominion over the fish of the sea, and over the fowl of the air, and over every living thing that moveth upon the earth.

29.   And God said, Behold, I have given you every herb bearing seed, which *is* upon the face of all the earth, and every tree, in which *is* the fruit of a tree yielding seed; to you it shall be for meat.

30.   And to every beast of the earth, and to every fowl of the air, and to every thing that creepeth upon the earth, wherein *there is* life, *I have given* every green herb for meat: and it was so.

31.   And God saw every thing that he had made, and, behold, *it was* very good. And the evening and the morning were the sixth day.

CHAPTER ELEVEN

The Creation of Adam

BEFORE we can conclude our review of the sixth day of the creative work, we must note again how we have traced the successive work of prepartion in the five preceding days. During this time God has been preparing the temple for the presence of a worshipper. Up to the close of the work as reviewed in our last chapter, namely, the creation of the animal, the Heavenly Father has been finishing a house for a tenant.

But now suddenly and dramatically the account takes on a new and loftier phraseology, as the record tells of the creation of the worshipper to inhabit this temple. In the foregoing activities of God, He has been depicted as outside His creation, directing by His mighty power certain forces in construction. There has been an attitude of aloofness in the repeated phrase, "Let there be;" but now He is represented as coming forth after consultation and with mature deliberation crowning all of His work by personally forming the last creature. So that of man alone it can be said, "He has been shaped by the hand of God and quickened by His divine breath."

Before proceeding to the evidence of design in this last act of creation, there are certain textual notes that we cannot avoid. Here, for instance, is, in the Scripture, the first suggestion of the Trinity. We not infrequently hear men say today that the Trinity is a New Testament doctrine that was apparently unknown to the Ancients. That this is not the case, however, is seen in the statement of this text. When God said, "Let *us* make man in *our* image, after *our* likeness," He was implying the multiplicity of personality that we call the Trinity. The plural word for God, *Elohim,* is here coupled with the singular, *Bara,* to create. Thus we have a strange suggestion of a plurality of personality with a singular act of creation. The words above quoted, "in our image," and "after our likeness," have ever been a source of mystification to the careful student of the Scripture. Does this mean that God has arms, legs, eyes, ears, a nose, in a real body such as man possesses? The modernist is very fond of sneering at the childlike faith of the true believer and designates us as anthropomorphists. The word *anthropomorphism* does not necessarily frighten the intelligent believer, for he has the habit of taking words to pieces and seeing what they mean. The derivation of this word is simple: *anthropus,* the Greek word for man; *morphe,* the Greek word for bodily substance. We then have, according to our enemies, a conception of God in human substance.

To which we reply, "What other conception of God can we have?" If God does not reveal Himself to man in human terms, it is an absolute impossibility for man to have any conception of God. If the Deity revealed Himself to man in terms of angelic language, He must remain perfectly unknown to men, for we do not speak that language. How useless would it be for God to seek to reveal Himself to man in a language common to dogs or cats! That is not our mental realm; so the amazing grace of God is seen in this condescension. For the sake of a contact with His creature, He will stoop to express Himself in terms that humanity can comprehend, that they may have fellowship and communion with Him.

But reason also comes to our aid and suggests that God is a Person, Whom we call the Heavenly Father. Since it is outside the realm of philosophy to conceive of personality apart from some sort of bodily substance, if God is a Person we cannot believe in Him as a gaseous mass permeating the ether. Whatever that substance or bodily feature of God may consist of, it is spiritual to the highest degree. We have only the revelation

of the Lord Jesus Christ, of Whom it is written, "No man hath
seen God at any time. The Only Begotten Son, Who was in
the bosom of the Father, He hath showed Him forth" (John
1:18). In the humanity of Jesus Christ we have the ultimate
expression of God seeking to identify Himself with man.

It is evident to human reason that God is not a mist, a vapor,
or a gas permeating all space, as He is revealed as a Person.
We cannot conceive of personality apart from some bodily
form, and He who is called "Our Father in Heaven" must have
some substance and form. So we hear Paul, the inspired, stating of Jesus in His pre-incarnate glory . . . "Who existed in
the form of God." The Greek word here used is *morphe,*
which is the basis of our modern term *morphology.* This is
the science of the gross bodily structure; so that Jesus is thus
described as "existing in the bodily substance" of God.

Now, in some sense that human reason cannot clarify, God
created man after God's image and His likeness. These words
have very exact significance, as when Jesus illustrated them in
the use of the tax money. We remember He called for a coin,
and said, "Whose *image* and superscription is this?" When
His hearers replied, *"It is the image of Caesar,"* they were simply stating that the head upon the coin bore some resemblance
to the great emperor. In that same significant manner it is
stated of man that he is the image and the likeness of God.

There is also the possibility that the phrase, "In His image,
and after His likeness," may have an allegorical application as
well. It is clearly stated in the Scripture that man is triune in
his nature and living. As God is a Trinity, so the shadow of
this figure is mirrored as well in man. In First Thessalonians,
chapter five, and verse twenty-three, we read: ". . . and I pray
God that your entire spirit, and soul, and body may be preserved blameless until the appearing of Jesus Christ our
Lord."

Here, then, is suggested the application in the spiritual
realm. As God is one Being, but is manifested as Father, Son,

and Holy Spirit, these three Persons may be also mirrored in the trinity that is man, body, soul, and spirit. Although sadly warped by sin, and with its beauty dimmed by the ages of iniquity, man still bears that image of God, the Triune.

We further note in the analysis of this text that from the very beginning God's plan was for a family. It has been contended by the ignorant and unlearned that the creation of woman does not come until the second chapter of Genesis. Indeed, we recently had a contender who objected to the doctrine of inspiration because of the absence of the woman in the first chapter of Genesis. He said that there were two accounts of creation, and that they were in vital conflict with each other. In the first chapter of Genesis, Adam alone is mentioned, and the woman is left out. In the second chapter the woman is mentioned, in a separate and conflicting story of creation, differing altogether from the account in chapter one.

We pointed out to him that his error was a lack of intelligent reading of the text! For the first chapter clearly states "male and *female* created He them." Also we sought to show the critic that the second chapter of Genesis is but an addition to the details of the first chapter. When Moses tells the entire story of the six days' work of God, he sketches in the broad outline with swift strokes, until the entire picture emerges to our understanding. Then he retraces his path, and adds later details that he did not use in the broad outline, but gives the additional data only where it is vitally needed; so that he adds certain illuminations to the work of only three of the days.

The critic objected that if this were so, Moses would have put the entire story in *one* chapter, not in two! How marvelously this illustrates the ability of the keen mentality that would contradict the Book that God has written! We merely pointed out to this "seeker (?) after light" that when Moses wrote, *he did* put the entire record into one chapter! In the ancient Hebrew manuscripts, the book of Genesis is *all one chapter!* From the first word to the last, there is no single division, no comma, period, or mark of punctuation of any kind whatsoever. The chapter and verse division that is so common to our own day is a modern innovation of the translators: and in some instances these chapter divisions are made right in the very middle of a verse! It may be that our present division is made in an unfortunate place in the manuscript; indeed, that fact is evident! Moses here tells the story of a Divine Week; which is seven days, and the "first chapter" ends with the sixth, not the seventh day.

How marvelous is the honesty of the critic! When we showed this objector that Moses put the account in one unbroken story, true to type, he replied, "Well, I don't believe him, anyhow!" There are many thoughtless and unbelieving ones that fall into this same condemnation, however, for many still echo this same objection.

They must have missed the significance of the phrase, "so God created man in His own image, after His likeness, *male and female, created He them.*" When God blessed them for propagation it implies He meant man and woman, for no man alone is capable of reproducing a family! Since this blessing has never been lost, but survived the judgment on sin, man still has the high and the holy privilege of sharing with God the power of creation in the fulfillment of the destiny of the human race.

The most significant phrase in the Scripture dealing with the work of this day is the thirty-first verse, "And God saw every thing that He had made, and, behold, it was very good." We may then read as a law of interpretation that whatever of evil or vice is now apparent in the physical universe came after God had finished His part and is not of His will. To illustrate this law, let us go to the pathogenic organisms called bacteria, microbes, and bacilli, which cause disease and death in the human body. These growths are alive. A bacterium is as much a living creature as is an elephant, or a cow, or a human being. Since the Scripture makes the definite declaration that "Christ created all things, and without Him hath not anything been made that hath been made," the naturalistic philosopher has reasoned that Jesus must then be responsible for disease.

A careful study of the science of bacteriology, however, would demonstrate that this is a false conclusion. The premise is sound, but the logic of the conclusion is faulty. Every microscopic organism that is known to be pathogenic to the human race has a benevolent task to perform. Without the bacteria this world could not continue for ninety days in its wild state in nature. We state as a basic premise of logic that a good thing in a wrong place loses its benevolent nature. As an instance, we must have water to live; we drink this fluid and the stomach receives it. But water in the lungs brings death! We must have air to live, but air normally belongs in the lungs. Put it in the blood stream and the result is death!

A good thing in the wrong place changes its nature. In the world in which we live the bacteria are essential for growth and for life, and for cleanliness as well. However, they do not belong in the blood stream of man, so when these micro-organisms leave their sphere and intrude into that place for which they were never intended, havoc is raised with God's perfect plan. We have reason to believe that were it not for the fact of sin these creatures and all others would have kept their fore-ordained places, and these difficulties would never have arisen.

We come now to the climax of this most marvelous chapter in all literature known to man, in words the simplicity of which is not beyond the reasoning power of a child, but the grandeur of which has baffled the analysis of the deepest philosopher. Moses sets forth the fact that the creative work of God is climaxed in the human realm. To establish the truth of this contention, certain specific statements made by Moses must be the subject of our investigation. In the realm of the allied sciences that touch the field of anthropology we will conclude our reasoning concerning the credibility of Genesis I, the foundation chapter of the entire Bible.

It is here stated that man was created by a specific fiat of the Deity. To refute this, men who are unwilling to receive and recognize the power of God in creation have produced the weird theory of Theistic Evolution. By this they state that God's part in the matter was a minor part. He created the first tiny living cell and endued it with power to multiply and change, violated all present known laws of biology, and by a series of miraculous transmutations produced all living things that are now or ever have been, climaxing in a creature called man. This is a hopeless attempt to ride two horses that are headed in the opposite directions! This theory of Theistic Evolution limits God in His power to create a specific being, and denies Him the authority demanded by the creation account in Genesis. It also violates the clear teaching of this text.

The theory of Theistic Evolution starts man as far down in the scale of minute things as is conceivably possible. Then by gradual and continued ascent it brings man to the head of creation's present order, of which he is recognized as lord. In other words, in this theory, man started low and has continually ascended from plane to higher plane.

The theory of specific creation, on the other hand, starts man *higher than he now is!* It has him in the hour of his origin a sinless, perfect being, dwelling in instant communion with his Maker. The record of the Word states that from this high place man fell until in his sin he became lower than the animals of the field. From this low and fallen state man never rose until Jesus Christ came and lifted him.

It has been our pleasure to see many magnificent and skilled riders riding two horses at the same time. We have noticed, however, that these equestrians were careful to keep their two steeds close together, *and both going in the same direction!* We never saw a man ride two horses headed in opposite directions.

Which of these "horses" shall we ride? The scientific, biological, and philosophical nonsense of human reason, called "evolution," or the clear-cut statement of the Word of God, "creation"? Before coming to a conclusion, let us follow the evidence in anthropology and its kindred sciences and see if they can establish the credibility of the statement of Moses that God created man "in His own image and after His likeness."

The first evidence of creative design that we shall advance is the morphological argument derived from man's general shape, or image. Some time ago we were amazed to hear a paper read by a man of science criticising the shape and structure of the human body. He said that it was very evident that the human body was not the result of intelligence and design. It seemed to be put together in such a haphazard fashion as to obviate the suggestion of intelligence. He said that there were appendages here and there, such as arms, legs, etc., that were subject to the buffets of hostile nature and frequently were broken and injured. To quote this man in his exact words, he said, "Now, if I should design a body for man I would design it scientifically, with nothing adhering to the outside that could be broken, damaged, or injured. I would make man a spheroid, thus able to resist unexpected pressure from every conceivable angle" (We have seen many men in recent years who were rapidly approaching this ideal!). Somewhat amazed, we arose and asked the privilege of a question. The privilege being granted, there ensued this conversation:

"Do we understand you correctly to say that if you were designing a body for man you would make it a perfect spheroid? A round ball, with no appendages on the outside?"

"That is exactly what I said."

"Then this is the question: When you had designed this round body with nothing adhering to the exterior, where would you put the emergency brake to stop him when he started down hill? We presume the law of gravity would still be in effect."

There was general laughter over the assembly at this, when in some anger the professor said that the question was too silly even to answer! So we never found out how this rotund being was to be able to ascend and descend hills with no spurs or brakes to aid or hinder. In spite of this very learned dissertation, we will still insist that the very shape of man marks him as a creature of God's designing.

First, he is in all ways distinct from the animal. There is no animal that can maintain the erect position that is natural to man. Some time ago, in debating with one of the foremost medical doctors in America, this great authority stated that man had recently acquired his upright posture. He advanced as his reason the fact of hernia, which is common to man. From this he deduced that man has only recently learned to walk on his hind legs, so that the visceral cavity is not capable of sustaining this tremendous weight for which man is not designed.

In rebuttal, we asked the doctor to explain how it is that if hernia is the result of a recently acquired upright posture, this malady is so common in dogs and hogs and Jersey cattle! With a humorous acknowledgement of surrender, the doctor stated, "I did not know that hernia was common to dogs and cattle, as I am a surgeon and not a veterinarian. However, I am glad to know that dogs have hernia. I have always been very fond of dogs and this shows how human they are."

Now what are we to conclude? That man is very like the animal because he has hernia? The animal is very human because he has the same! The conclusion is inescapable that the good doctor had not thought his way through this, as he later confessed.

The reason for the ease of the upright posture common in the human family is a rather strange structure of their lower extremities. There is no animal that naturally and normally walks in an upright posture. If you note the giant apes that are called manlike — such as the gorilla, the chimpanzee, the orang-utan, and the baboon — in their natural state they walk in a slouched-over position. As they ramble through the jungle they rest their weight on the back of their front paws. As they amble along, they sway from side to side with a curious motion, and rise to their hind legs only under stress of great excitement, strong suspicion, or when reaching for food. Everywhere they sustain this unnatural position by grasping some object with their front paws. Their posture at rest is a peculiar squat; and because of the strange alignment of the gluteus maximus it is extremely inconvenient for such a creature to attempt to sit on a chair.

Of course, you may teach a dog or horse to walk for a few steps on its hind legs, but the disagreeable experience is shortened as soon as the animal can express its own desire. On the other hand, man is extremely uncomfortable in anything but the upright posture, or in the comfortable position assumed when resting in an easy chair.

We are very careful to state that the evidence of the abdominal structure has been highly overemphasized. We are told that the various organs are tied in such a way as they would be tied were we designed to walk on four legs. Of course they are! Gravity affects every substance that adheres to this planet, and if those organs were not tied in their present positions they would drop into one ruptured mass to the bottom of the abdominal wall, and death would quickly follow. Apparently these wise philosophers have forgotten that man lies prone in sleep, and were these organs tied in any other position than this which the Creator has designed for them, the comfort of sleep would be denied to man. So then, since the body of man is distinct in its outline and general morphology from the animals to which we are in no sense related, we see here an evidence of design.

The symmetry and the beauty of feature, the changing expression of the eyes, the flashing light of the smile, and the mo-

bility of countenance must all be included in this differenti-
ation.

Perhaps the most conclusive single proof of man's separation from the world of the animal would be in the recent discovery of a remarkable re-agent by the Parke Davis Laboratory.
This has been designated "anti-human precipitant," and has
been widely received. If any substance from any living creature is put into the test tube and the re-agent added, it gives
an instant reaction, telling inevitably whether the substance
came from man or from an animal. Now if there *is* a re-agent,
a chemical substance that will infallibly determine the difference between man and the animal, how can we be so ignorant
and unscientific as to say "man and the other animals?"

The second great evidence of design in the human structure
must be found in the mechanical perfection of osteology. Osteology is the science of bone structure. In the amazing mechanical perfection of the osseous frame of the human body,
there are manifold evidences of design. Indeed, it may be laid
down as a basic fact in all morphology that every mechanical
principle save one, is found in the human body. There has
never yet been discovered the operation of the principle called
the wheel, which seems to be man's only original contribution
to the world of mechanics. All else, however, is discovered in
the human body.

The instrument called the camera is a reproduction of the
mechanics of vision. The lens, the diaphragm, the film, and
all the component parts of the instrument of photography are
absolute replicas of the principle found in human vision.

The Stillson wrench, used by all plumbers and men who
must grasp a round object, is but the curling grip of the thumb
and finger transmuted to an instrument of steel. The operation of the pincers for gripping and holding is but the adaptation of the grip of the human hand. Even the old instrument
called the "bellows," used by the village blacksmith, is a modi-
fication of the human diaphragm which inflates and deflates

the lungs. It may surprise some of our readers to learn that the motor that drives the modern automobile owes its invention to a functioning organ of the body! There never was an internal combustion engine that operated satisfactorily, until a British physician took a French mechanic into his surgery, and showed him how the valves of the human heart function! Transmitting this idea to iron and steel, the "gasoline engine" is the result! Now if man is to be praised for the *application* of the valve principle, what measure of homage should we accord Him Who *invented* that principle? If man may be called ingenious for rediscovering these principles in his body and applying them to his daily labor, how much more is demonstrated the genius of the Creator Who has originated those principles.

To apply our thought to osteology alone, the principle of brace and counter-brace and all other engineering basic laws are seen in the bony structure of man. There is, for instance, that amazing triangulation of the scapula and clavicle. This triangulation not only maintains the rigid posture of the torso but is responsibile also for the power of the arm. The first member in this osseous triangulation is the scapula, commonly known as the shoulder blade. The second member is the upright column of the backbone, and the clavicle completes the cycle. In this triangulation the entire structure of the shoulder and upper arm develops its tremendous power. The humerus, the large bone of the upper arm, ends in a ball. The small end of the scapula is a socket in which the humerus articulates. There is a basic principle of engineering, that all stress exerted at one end of a member will be evenly distributed over the other end of the same member. Here then is where the arm gets its power. Articulating against the small round end of the scapula, the thrust of the humerus is absorbed, the triangular shape of the shoulder blade widening out as it reaches the other end. Here it presses against six of the ribs, which act as springs. It makes contact with the lower three, and braces against the upper three by means of the rhomboid muscles. This develops the principle that would be phrased in engineering terms, the counter recoil buffers.

All the pressure exerted against the small end of the scapula is evenly distributed against these spring-like buffers at the wide end, and the shock is absorbed and distributed so as to give the tremendous leverage created by the motion of the upper arm. This testifies to the fact of design, in words that the simplest, as well as the wisest, can understand.

At the other extreme there is the remarkable development of the femur. The eminent George Van Amber Brown has called our attention to an amazing evidence of design in this section of the human anatomy. Structural engineers have been searching for a long time for the perfect truss, one that will stand the stress of twenty thousand pounds per square inch. When such a member is developed, it will be received as mechanical perfection. There is only one place in nature where this is found. The trabeculae of the human femur are so curved as to enable that member to stand the exact pressure of twenty thousand pounds per square inch! Thus the largest bone in the human frame has been designed and protected by some engineering genius to the exact formula that would be recognized as engineering perfection. Certainly true intelligence cannot receive this as entirely accidental! Man in all his genius has not been able to recapitulate this one member in his mechanical conquests.

The amazing genius of the Creator is further seen in the various types of extremities. In man we have the member called the hand, by the aid of which he has been able to subdue the earth, and bring it into obedience to his will. But the quadrumanes are not so. These gigantic apes may be classed as four handed creatures, but because they do not possess the peculiar blessing of such a thumb as is common to man their physical powers are limited.

In the fish it is the fin, in the lion a paw, in the horse a hoof, in the bird a claw: but man has the blessing of the extremity called the hand. His conquest of the arts and sciences, his remarkable subjugation of the powers of nature, the amazing edifice that is his home, and all that he has been able to accomplish, may be, in fact, attributed to the ingenuity which God lavished on him in creation. There is not a single articulating osseous member of the entire human frame that does not testify to the reality of creation and the amazing evidence of design in the human form.

If this is so in osteology, it is more eminently so *in the science called osteometry.* This is the science of the mathematical relationship of one bone to the other. It is so precise a science that, given any bone of the human body, we can measure it exactly and determine the size of every other bone in that same body from this one member. In the textbooks of osteometry, charts are given by which, at a glance, we can reconstruct the entire frame from a few tiny phalanges, from one rib, a patella, or any other bone that chances to be in our possession. We recognize that mathematics are always the result of intelligence, so if the human body is created with such a fine mathematical relationship that the smallest bone of the human foot will instantly give us the exact size of the entire skull, how can we say that accident or chance is responsible? Surely so marvelous a mathematical perfection as osteometry pleads for can be ascribed only to creation by an Intelligent Being, who so designed the body of man!

The author has dug from the earth considerably over 3,000 human skeletons in the course of his research, and has ever been impressed with the amazing symmetry of the human skeleton: every bone fitting exactly into the structure so finely that whether finger or toe, rib or skull, each is found in the required relation to every other one. Of course, there are exceptions, phenomenal, due to disease or accident, as in the case of osteomyelitis or some other disease which gives the bone an anomalous development, or causes deformation. These exceptions, however, leave their mark indelibly upon the bone, so it is impossible to confuse the issue with these freaks of circumstance. We conclude again that the science of osteometry as applied to the human frame is a testimony of the genius of God in design and creation.

In the independent functioning of the organs, there is not only a fresh evidence of design but a kindly provision of the Creator. The entire life of the body depends upon the efficient operation of organs and parts, the names of which are not known to most of us. But if a man does not know the difference between the oesophagus and the pylorus, the duodenum and broca's area, and between the others, how then is it possible for him to supervise with intelligence the functioning of these vital principles? Fortunately, he doesn't have to! If a man had to eat just one meal intelligently, mentally directing every operation, he would never proceed past the third or fourth mouthful. The operation of chewing, digestion by the co-operation of saliva glands, the myriad functions necessary to swallowing, the peristaltic action of the stomach, and all the marvelous processes essential to the assimilation of one meal would occupy so much of his time that the rest of his system would run riot! But the lungs go on breathing without any mental oversight; the liver, the kidneys, the heart all function smoothly in a normal body without any direction from the mental center. Since it is impossible to conceive of a continued operation and expended force without supervision, we are faced at once in the functioning of the organs with a benevolent design of an Intelligent Creator. Only those who are really ignorant of the amazing functions of the body will disregard such proof as this.

However, we are used to finding ignorance in strange places. Some years ago we lectured in the city of Fresno, in California. We had a number of students in regular attendance from the State Teachers' College, located in that city. On the faculty was a professor, an unbeliever, who rather opposed the attendance of his students at the evening lectures. The students would absorb ideas from the speaker at the evening hour and present them in class the next day. Then they would come back the following night with their professor's rebuttal. This informal debate continued to amuse and delight us, until one one day some of these students said that the professor had shown them by a sketch on the board that there was evidence that design was not manifested in the human body. He based this contention on the peculiar angle at which the oesophagus joined the stomach.

This teacher maintained that if intelligence were used in designing the body it would eliminate this angle and bring the oesophagus straight down in the center, joining the top of the stomach with hindering valves, so that gravity might aid in swallowing the food. His contention was that food may lump at that lower end and block the tube. The students replied, "It never does," and the professor replied, "Some day it might."

Evidently this man had never heard of the peristaltic muscles of the stomach which churn and grind and wrest the food in the process of digestion. If the Lord had known no more about mechanics than this professor and had put the oesophagus where the teacher wished it to be, every time we swallowed a morsel of food, peristalsis would chuck it right out the front door again the way it came in!

We cannot fail in such a paper to note also the vestigial organs with which the body is assumed to be replete. These organs are presumed to be useless, having been left to us as an evolutionary heritage from our primitive animal ancestors! These are supposed to be organs which once functioned in the animal bodies of our distant forefathers, and are now no longer useful to their human descendants. Thus the phrase, "vestigial organs." We have heard it remarked that there are some two hundred and seventy-seven of these rudimentary organs, but five is the largest list we have seen. It always struck us as a bit immodest on the part of man to say, "There are in my body five organs, the purpose of which I do not know. Therefore they can have no use or function." If the usefulness of our structure were limited to our knowledge of that structure, most of us would be in a sad fix indeed!

More recent knowledge of the body has reduced these so-called vestigial organs in number until as far as we know all have disappeared. A case in point is the tonsil, which was supposed to have no known use in the human body. We have now learned that up to the age of three the tonsil is vitally essential to the development of the human body. Operating with the pituitary gland it generates a serum (the tonsil being a ductless gland) which aids in the normal growth and development of the young body. The more careful and modern up-to-date specialists are reluctant to remove the tonsils until after the age of three. It is practically conceded by specialists that by the age of five the tonsil has served its purpose and should gradually begin to absorb. The false conditions of so-called civilization, however, have hindered the body in much of its normal development so that this absorption may long be delayed and in some cases completely inhibited here. In that case, surgery may be essential. In its natural state, however, there is a purpose and a functioning reason for every organ in the body.

Those who have pondered over the evidences of design in the frame of man have seen specific creation applied in the amazing system of the distribution of blood. Moses was indeed right when he said, "The life of the flesh is in the blood," and this blood is essential for the continuance of life in every part of the human system. Indeed if it were possible to have a technique of dissection that would leave the blood distribution system intact, we would have in that system an outline of the entire morphology of the body. Every cell in the body must ultimately get its quota of the blood, and the genius demonstrated in this system would appall the human who had to recapitulate a mechanism as extensive and perfect as this.

When digestion has been completed in the stomach and the intestine, the food cells are divided into their component parts and fed into the blood stream. The blood picks them up and takes them into the veins, and like little freight cars loaded with delicacies, the blood cells fly about the system carrying this food to the outer borders of the domain that is man. As the empty cars return they are loaded down with the debris from past meals and the whole task of feeding the body is carried on by these busy blood cells constantly renewing and rebuilding the parts.

We were somewhat surprised some time ago to have a professor emeritus at the University of Pennsylvania argue against design in creation, because of the presence of vascular valves. He said that these valves in the human body are not found in the torso, but begin to make their appearance in the upper part of the lower extremities. Now thus he reasoned that man had developed his upright posture in his evolution from the beast, because he said a four-footed creature would not need those abdominal valves. Evidently the professor had forgotten a good deal of his comparative anatomy. The fact of the matter is, that valves in the human body appear at different points in varying numbers in every individual human frame. These valves are safety devices produced by a convolution of the medina entima, very much after the fashion of the check valve which is used in modern mechanics. These valves appear at the exact strategic point where the outward thrust of the blood begins to lose its imparted velocity.

At that point where the power of the heart-beat is so weakened that the blood may slow down and back up, these valves are located. Operating on the principle of the check-valves, they prevent back flow until thrust of the beat of the heart pushes the blood through. In that momentary pause between two beats, as the blood starts to rush back, these valves close and hold the blood in place. The next beat of the heart again thrusts the blood through, and by that built-up pressure at strategic points in this fashion, the blood is forced to the outermost extremity of the body. In the torso of man where gravity is pulling down and aiding the stream of blood in its outgoing impulse, these valves do not appear. In the body of the long-barrel, four-footed animals, where gravity does not so aid, there *are* such abdominal valves, which according to this professor, are evidence *against* the theory of evolution! So that in the bone or the blood, wherever we look, there is evidence of specific creation and that design which testifies of the truth of creation.

To illustrate the power of the body to continue with that impulse granted it at creation, let us suppose this situation: On the outskirts of the city where you live there is a large factory employing thousands of people. The heart of that factory is a great steam engine whose pulsing, driving power spins the wheels and turns the belts that drive a myriad of machines. There are drill presses, trip-hammers, lathes, saws, and power-driven machines of all varieties. This factory is a bit obsolete, and the owner comes to you with a strange proposition, saying, "I want my factory renewed. How much would you charge me to build the entire building over? The walls, the roof, the ceiling, the floor, the windows, all must be renewed. I want a new engine that will drive that factory. Every part of that gigantic steam plant must be overhauled, and new pieces put in where the old ones were, and while you are at it, I want every foot of shafting replaced by fresh steel. Every belt must be taken away and a new one put in place. Every machine must be taken out and a new machine put in. I will give you this contract on condition that you will guarantee to do this work in such fashion that the mill does not close down one minute night or day while you work! No one machine must quit working, no one belt or wheel must be idle. Not one of the thousands of employees must be laid off for a single minute. Day and night this mill must turn out its usual products while you build the entire thing over. How much will this job cost?"

You look in surprise at this man and question his mental ability. How utterly inconceivable that such a huge piece of reconstruction could occur under those conditions; yet every twenty-eight days that thing is done in the human body. In this brief time the cells of the human body all die and are born again. Thus the cells of the heart are renewed, and the old engine never misses a beat. Every organ in the body is renewed by regeneration and never ceases to function. The two thousand billion cells of the body are born again, and not one single organ misses a beat or loses a moment of its active work while the whole thing is reconstructed. Even the house that holds these machines, called organs, is renewed approximately once every month, and the miracle that man cannot accomplish is performed by a function that God ordained in the hour of creation.

How heedless and utterly beyond the power of reasoning is the naturalistic philosopher who says all this came by accident and chance, and fails to see therein the element of design!

As a further expression of the God-like image of man given to him in creation we would argue his mentality. He is blessed with a type of memory that nothing else in creation possesses. We are, of course, familiar with the apparent memory feats of such a creature as the horse or the dog. These, however, learn by rote and habitual acquiescence. Things repeated in one physical performance after another soon become as natural as a characteristic, and the things which animals thus learn are peculiarly different from the memory feats of man. We cannot conceive of a troop of chimpanzees (which are reputed to be the highest developed mentally of all animals) performing on a lighted stage "The Merchant of Venice," "Romeo and Juliet," or "Midsummer Night's Dream"! No ape can act as prompter to the actors of a grand opera, and the memory feats of man mark him as far above the beast as the angels are above the human.

This same thing is seen in his power of abstract thought. It is natural and instinctive for man to reason from cause to effect, and by these powers, possessed by no animal, marvelous things are accomplished by him.

This may be illustrated in the realm of music. Many creatures (like the birds) have a native song, but man alone is a composer. We have heard it said that only the western meadow lark has anything approaching a scale. This bird has a song of five notes in the minor, which is the nearest thing to a chromatic scale to be found in nature. But a man by his power of abstract thought is able to write and form melodies, though he himself is not gifted with the power of song. A man who cannot himself sing a note may take unto himself a sheet of lined paper and make upon it marks of such significance that another man sitting at a pipe organ will make the air mellow with matchless music mentally produced by the man who himself had no song. The man who cannot himself sing may be responsible for the beauty of an entire philharmonic concert. This power to render musical expression by some instrument of mechanical construction is one of the most amazing evidences of creative genius that the human family affords. Not able himself to sing, a man invents a violin, a grand piano, a silver-toned trumpet, a seven-stringed harp of Terpander, and scores of others that nature cannot rival. His vocal expression in speech, the universal moral nature of man, and a thousand other kinesthetic instances may well be considered by those who possess the leisure. Time and space will not here permit their mention.

The main argument for a special creation, however, is the one great fact that raises man above the level of the beast, namely, the universal consciousness of God. There is no such thing in all this world as a natural atheist. A few men, moved to bitterness by the circumstances of life, have attacked the fact of God. A few other sadly muddled souls have become be-fuddled by the small amount of learning which one mind may absorb, and in the pride of their puny accomplishments have declared themselves to be greater than He! Such have de-nied His very existence, but these sad freaks of circumstances which we find only in so-called "civilized" circles are generally the result of an unsound philosophy on the part of those who are liberally *mis*-educated!

Atheism is as foreign to the nature of man as is song to the snapping turtle. If we were asked to define in one argument the first difference between man and beast, we would put it in these words: There is no animal so high in the scale of devel-opment that it worships God; there is no man so low that he lacks this trait. No matter how far you get off the beaten tracks of civilization or how low a tribe may be in culture, they have their consciousness of God. Even among the wild tribes of the Upper Orinoco it is customary for them to take a bit of blue clay, mold it into a weird image like unto nothing on the earth, the waters beneath, or the sky above. Decorating this outlandish monstrosity with monkey fur and toucan feath-ers, they bow down and worship the intangible idea of God which is made concrete by this physical image. The humblest black in the heart of Africa has this in common with the sa-vant of white civilization: *We are all conscious of the fact of God!* This is the last residuum of that mighty fellowship which Adam possessed when he was created by the hand of God and in-breathed by His divine breath.

Thus simply, then, the whole story of man can be told in three words. Not evolution, not civilization, and not human accomplishment.

These three words would be

Creation
Degeneration
Re-creation

It is evident to the earnest and thoughtful that man was created by God. Even at this distant day it is apparent to even the casual observer that man still bears this image, even though it has been ruined by sin. His entire nature testifies to this appalling fact of a fall, with evidences we cannot disregard. Not only of the antediluvians could the Spirit complain, "Every imagination of their hearts was evil in His sight continually"; it might just as truthfully be stated today. The body in which we dwell for the years of our earthly tarrying, no less than our mental nature, is marked and seamed by the ravages of sin.

So far has man got from his original condition in creation that it is common, nay, even habitual, for men to be daily guilty of sins and incests so vile that they are never dreamed of by the beasts of the field! Lechery and vice that would shame the animals, are committed by men: all as a result of the degeneration that sin has wrought in human lives. So much so, that the entire story of human history has been one of bloodshed, suffering, warfare, and battle. All this has come because of this same dread fact: man has been ruined by sin.

If we had to stop there, in the face of this black and awful picture, this book would never have been written! But we remember that shadows are only possible because of light; and the blacker the shadow, the brighter must be the light that makes it visible. So with this record of human failure and bleak tragedy: it is made more apparent by the light of God's grace, in the cross of Jesus Christ.

Creation *was* followed by degeneration; but the whole story is not told without the blessed fact of *re*generation! So we can complete the picture and close the cycle by noting the fact that the Lord Jesus gave His blessed blood on the cross, that men might be born again, and saved from the effects of their sin.

To that end we have presented these chapters, in the hope that we might appeal to those whose powers of reason are not too sadly blunted by sin. To some, perhaps, this line of evidence from science will make no appeal, which we can only regret. If reason and intelligence are dethroned by sin, and lust is enshrined in their place, we may regret and sympathize; but we cannot then aid.

In the hope, however, that by descending to the lower plane of science and reason we may induce some to ascend with us to the higher plane of faith, this record is offered.

Is it not reasonable to presume that if God did create man to be His fellow and companion, He would seek to reveal Himself to that man? Not only reasonable, but historically and scientifically demonstrated! The first revelation He made of Himself was in the page of nature. When this natural revelation was obstructed by sin, then He revealed Himself more firmly in that Book we call the Bible, thus supplementing the scientific with the historical. And, to crown it all, He fulfilled His revelation in the sending of the Saviour, Jesus Christ, the last revelation God has made or ever will make to men.

Indeed, John has told the whole story when he said: "But these things are written, that ye might believe that Jesus is the Christ, the Son of God, and so believing, have life everlasting in His name."

The conclusion must be written by the reader. Reason will tell you that science is correct here; we were created by God.

Conscience will convict you of the fact of sin!

Then an intelligent and logical decision will lead you to exercise your reason, and turn to the Lord Jesus as a Saviour from sin, and receive that re-creation that the Holy Spirit alone can bring! Thus will be fulfilled the climax and the promise of Second Corinthians, chapter five, verse seventeen, contained in these words:

"Therefore, if any man be in Christ Jesus, *this is new creation*: old things are passed away, behold, all things are made new!"

THE END

BS 651 .R55 1937
Harry Rimmer
Modern Science and the
Genesis Record